BEEKEEPING TECHNIQUES

BEEKEEPING TECHNIQUES

ALEX S. C. DEANS

N.D.B., F.R.E.S.

Head of Beekeeping Department
North of Scotland College of Agriculture

OLIVER & BOYD

EDINBURGH AND LONDON

OLIVER AND BOYD LTD

Tweeddale Court
Edinburgh 1

39a Welbeck Street
London W.1

First published 1963

PRINTED IN GREAT BRITAIN BY
OLIVER AND BOYD LTD., EDINBURGH

CONTENTS

		Page
Introduction		xi
Technique		
1.	Bee Breeding	1
	Inbreeding	2
	Mother/son mating	3
	Brother/sister mating	4
	Instrumental insemination	5
	Maintenance of colony vigour	8
2.	Queen Rearing	10
	Methods	14
	Cell grafting	18
	Formation of mating nuclei	19
	Multiple mating of queen bees	21
3.	Queen Appraisal	25
	Determination of egg-laying rates of queen bees	27
	Example calculation	27
4.	Queen Introduction	31
5.	Swarm Control	35
	Method	36
6.	Honey Production	41
	Forage area and foraging range	41
	Migratory beekeeping	42
	Production of bees	42
	Method of honey production	45
	Time of supering	45
	Foundation v. built out combs	46
	Frame staggering	47

Technique

    6. HONEY PRODUCTION *Continued*   Page

        Honey removal   47
        Comb storage   49
        The use of the queen excluder   49
        Honey processing equipment   50
        Honey containers   52
        Honey heating cabinet   53
        Creamed honey   53

    .7 HEATHER HONEY PRODUCTION   55
        Locality   55
        The brood chamber   57
        Methods of honey production   59
        Transporting the colonies   61
        Settling down and liberating the bees   62
        The nature of ling heather honey   63
        ' Standards ' for pressed ling heather honey   63

    8. HONEY JUDGING   67
        Class : Liquid honey   67
                Granulated honey   69
                Comb honey   70
                Ling heather honey   71
                Wax   71
                Mead   72
        General Points   72

    9. BEE DISEASE CONTROL AND DIAGNOSIS   73
        Acarine disease   74
        Method of using ' Folbex '   74
        Nosema disease   76
        Bee paralysis   77
        Poisoning   77
        European Foul Brood   78
        American Foul Brood   79
        Chilled brood   80

Technique
9. BEE DISEASE CONTROL AND DIAGNOSIS *Continued*   Page
        Sack brood   81
        Chalk brood   81
        Diagnosis of acarine disease   81
            nosema disease   83
            amoeba disease   85
            bee paralysis   86
            poisoning   87
            European Foul Brood   87
            American Foul Brood   89
            sack brood   90
            chalk brood   90
            addled brood   91
            chilled brood   91
        How to take a sample of bees   91

10. MICROSCOPY   93
        Essential apparatus   93
        Preparation of material for microscopic examina-
            tion   95
        The Mid Gut : Detailed technique   97
        Preparation of wings, sting, legs, etc.   101

11. THE POLLEN ANALYSIS OF HONEY   104
        Definition   104
        Practical value   105
        Accuracy of pollen analysis   105
        Absolute pollen content of honey   109
        Honey-dew honeys   109
        Preparation of ' standard ' pollen slides   110
        Preparation of pollen sediment from honey   111
        Classification of pollen grains   115
        Identification of pollen grains   115

12. HONEY ANALYSIS   118
        Honey sugars   122
        Crystallisation   126

Technique

12. HONEY ANALYSIS *Continued*   Page

Fermentation   127

Determination of invert sugar in honey   131

    dextrose in honey   133

    colloid content of honey   134

    the total acid in honey expressed as the mg.

        equivalent   135

    ash in honey   136

    non-reducing sugar in honey   136

    the absolute number of pollen grains in honey   137

    pH of honey   138

    water content, specific gravity and refractive

        index of honey   139

13. CHROMATOGRAPHIC ANALYSIS OF HONEY   141

14. STATISTICAL TECHNIQUES   144

    REFERENCES   158
    BOOKS FOR FURTHER STUDY   160

ILLUSTRATIONS

Figs.   Page

1. Mother/son mating   3

2. Brother/sister mating   4

3. Graph showing increase in homozygosity   5

4. Back-cross to Male   8

5. and 7. Queen Rearing Tools   *facing* 16

6. Queen nursery frame   *facing* 17

8. Queen Marking Colours   26

9. Rate of Laying Table   28

10. 'Worth' Queen Cage   *facing* 32

11. and 12. Normal Colony Development: Phases 1 and 2   37

13.   ,,   ,,   Phase 3   39

14. Circular honey sections   *facing* 45

15. Graph showing relationship of egg laying to season of year   57

16. Arrangement of combs in brood chamber   58

17. Honey judging: class, liquid honey   68

18.   ,,   class, granulated honey   69

19.   ,,   class, comb honey   70

20.   ,,   class, wax   72

21. Frequency of occurrence of pollen   106

22. to 34. Micro-photographs of pollen grains   *between* 120-121

35. Looking down a ray of light   132

36. Histogram showing distribution of values for specific gravity of 20 honey samples   148

37. Symmetrical distribution of all values of the above   148

INTRODUCTION

It has been said that more books have been written about the honey bee than any other creature with the exception of man himself. In view of this it may appear to some that all aspects of the science and practice of Beekeeping must already be fully covered.

As in other crafts, much that is standard practice must remain unchanged but a living organism so unpredictable as the honey bee presents a challenge. New methods of management and variations of old ones are constantly being devised. A difficulty however arises from this in that the progressive beekeeper finds himself confronted by a multitude of techniques, old and new, all possessing some merit.

In this volume I have tried to avoid that weakness of most bee books, reiteration, and to present only those techniques which I have found to be efficient and as nearly as possible foolproof in operation. To have included all the methods of, for example, swarm control or queen introduction would have meant a volume of inordinate length.

Some techniques have been dealt with in detail, others merely outlined.

On the question of bee breeding I have tried to indicate the difficulties that arise in a practical breeding programme and the limitations to breeding techniques when applied to the honey bee.

The serious student of the bee must, sooner or later, wish to study at first hand, the intriguing anatomical structure of the insect. While a certain amount of information on practical bee anatomy is available it is scattered throughout specialised books and treatises and cannot readily be obtained by the student.

I have tried to present here reasonably simple techniques which should be of value to the student in practical anatomical studies.

The honey analysis techniques have been set out in some detail since this information is not, as far as I am aware, readily available elsewhere. While laboratory facilities are an advantage for many of the techniques given no specially complicated equipment is required and some pieces, e.g. the wax embedding oven, can easily be improvised.

Today, scientific workers all over the world are devoting a great deal of time to the investigation of beekeeping problems and the volume of literature produced is considerable. The competent research worker submits his results to the statistician who tests, mathematically, whether or not an obtained result could have arisen by chance. The science of statistics is of great importance in all research work and in order to help the serious student to understand what the statistician is up to I have tried to present, simply, a few of the elementary techniques used.

Serious study of the science of bee husbandry leads the student into many branches of technology. I hope in this volume that certain needs have been filled both in field and laboratory technology applicable to the study of the honey bee and that in carrying out the techniques the student will experience as much enjoyment as I have had in devising and proving them.

The pollen photographs and all the other illustrations are quite original and are here published for the first time.

*　　*　　*

I would like to thank the many beekeepers and scientific workers who have, wittingly or unwittingly, been of assistance to me in devising the techniques given in this book.

Thanks are also due to the publishers for valuable suggestions anent the format of the book.

' For it behoves the Beekeeper to be skilled in the preparation of things needful for apiculture and able in procuring the supply of necessaries for the bees: and inventive: and energetic and thoughtful and persevering as well as prompt: both kind and severe, both simple and crafty, both given to save and ready to steal: lavish and yet rapacious: both loving to give and covetous: cautious and yet enterprising and it behoves the man who will be a successful beemaster to have many other qualifications both by nature and by science.'

With apologies to XENOPHON: *Memorabilia* 3.

Technique No. 1

BEE BREEDING

From the beginning of husbandry in settled agricultural communities attention has been directed to the improvement of stock and crops. Throughout the years many so-called ' wild ' or primitive types of plant and animal have been subjected to breeding techniques, resulting in the present-day high quality animals and high yielding root, cereal and fruit crops.

Comparable progress has not been made in the ' improvement ' of the honey bee and the type we have in Europe today appears to differ little, if at all, from that tended by the prehistoric bee-keeper depicted in the Arana cave drawings. In other words, the honey bee appears to have been static in form for many centuries.

Before considering the various techniques used in the propagation of the honey bee it is important to get the problem of stock improvement in true perspective.

While honey bees appear to be subject to the same genetic laws as other forms of life it is important to appreciate that some quite formidable difficulties lie in the path of the would be ' bee improver '.

Honey bees, unlike e.g. pigs and cows, belong to the general category of lower animals and, it would appear, are not so ' pliable ' in the hands of the geneticist as other farm stock. Undoubtedly this is largely due to the great antiquity of the honey bee, as a biological type. It seems probable, from fossil evidence (Armbruster [1]) that the honey bee attained the peak of its development about 150 million years ago, which would account for the rigidity with which, as a genetic type, it is fixed.

The phenomenon of parthenogenesis further complicates any bee breeding programme but the greatest difficulty is due to the uncertainty of parentage control. Until the advent of improved techniques of instrumental insemination of queen bees, strict control of mating was not fool-proof. The value of instrumental insemination in general beekeeping practice is doubtful but as a laboratory tool for the geneticist its possibilities are clearly considerable.

In practice it is difficult to keep bees pure in the genetical sense. For example, if the colour of bee in any apiary is uniformly brown to black and an Italian or yellow type queen is introduced, within one season the progeny of any new young queens mated in the apiary will show some evidence of hybridisation. After two or three seasons the chances are that the colour of the bees in the entire apiary will show evidence of yellow parentage.

On the other hand, if bees in any region of northern Europe are kept free from crossing with southern European or north African types, they remain predominantly black or dark brown in colour: or if their original body colour showed traces of yellow, this gradually disappears and, after a decade of isolation, it again becomes uniformly dark.

If a beekeeper is satisfied that he possesses a useful strain of bee and he wishes to propagate it with a view to retaining its excellent qualities, adulteration of such stock must be precluded. Further, the desirable traits must be ' fixed ' by pure line breeding or inbreeding.

The purpose of inbreeding is to put the gene pairs in a homozygous condition and, further, to keep the genes in the ' line '. Inbreeding tends to sort out the genes by breaking up and reforming combinations so that undesirable characteristics, controlled by undesirable genes, are brought to light. Subsequently the undesirable types are eliminated by selection and the desirable retained, and maintained, by controlled mating. An increase in homogeneity may be brought about merely by inbreeding alone. For example, if one takes a plant, heterozygous for a single pair of genes and ' selfs ' it (i.e. brings about self fertilisation) half the offspring will be homozygous, and, if the process is repeated, the proportion of heterozygotes is halved in each generation. Unfortunately the technique of ' selfing ' cannot be applied in the case of the honey bee.

When inbreeding is practised the possibility exists that the viability of the strain may be reduced. This is a serious drawback and may give rise to all sorts of physical abnormalities in individuals, as well as sterility. In beekeeping practice abnormalities are rarely encountered but cases of addled brood (easily remedied by requeening) do arise and an analysis of the relevant circumstances usually indicates that inbreeding is responsible.

Where poor quality stock exists and where inbreeding has occurred, visible signs may take the form of European Foul Brood.

By definition, 'breeding' is taken to mean the systematic pairing of selected males and females which possess the characteristics the breeder considers desirable and which he wishes to perpetuate.

Such matings must be continued through successive generations until the desired type is produced. Once such a type is obtained it is necessary to evaluate the individuals of each generation and select, for further propagation, those which are breeding true and show full vigour. Two techniques of bee breeding may now be considered: (a) mother/son mating and (b) brother/sister mating.

Mother/son mating

If an unfertile, virgin queen is subjected to treatment with carbon dioxide gas, rapid 'ageing' takes place and egg production is stimulated. Eggs so produced are unfertile and give rise to drones. At maturity, semen may be taken from these drones and

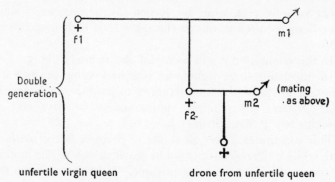

FIG. 1. Mother/son mating.

used, by means of the technique of instrumental insemination, to fertilise the virgin queen, thus giving a mother/son mating. This process may be repeated again and again (at any rate in theory) and, when it is repeated once, we have what is known as a 'double generation' (Fig. 1).

Brother/sister mating

In this case a virgin queen is mated to one of her brothers and, in the next generation, one of her daughters is mated to one of her sons. This is known as a ' single generation' (Fig. 2).

Of the two systems the first (theoretically) is the more efficient. It is estimated (Kalmus & Smith [2]) that the number of double generations in system (*a*) required to reduce impurity to 10% of its

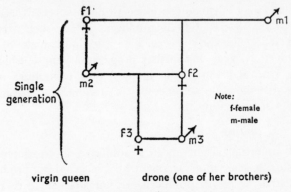

FIG. 2. Brother/sister mating.

former value is 3·32, while for system (*b*) the number of single generations required to obtain the same level of homogeneity is 10·86.

In this connection it will be useful also to study Fig. 3.

In translating these techniques into beekeeping practice it is important to realise the time required to produce single generations. System (*a*) requires approximately 60 days and (*b*) approximately 37 days (Palmer Jones [3]).

This constitutes a very slow rate of progress but it *would* be worth while if the objective could be reached. Using the mother/son system this does not seem possible. It has been shown that frequent handling of the queens in the process of insemination results in the chances of their final acceptance by the bees of the mating nuclei being reduced virtually to nil. Palmer Jones states ' it was soon apparent that the mother/son method of inbreeding was not practicable and it was abandoned and the brother/sister method alone employed. Forty one queens were inbred by the brother/sister method during the 1949/50 season:

38 of these were inbred for one generation and 3 were inbred for 2 generations. Twenty of those inbred for one generation were not accepted by the bees and were found dead after preliminary maltreatment. One queen of those inbred for two generations was lost. The extent to which inbreeding will be carried out will be governed to some degree by the hatchability of eggs of the inbred queen.'

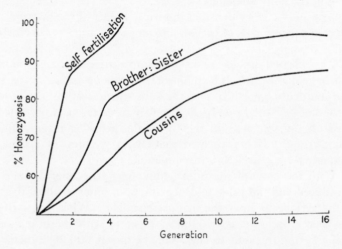

FIG. 3. Graph showing increase in homozygosity in relation to type of mating and number of generations involved.

Even assuming the technique of instrumental insemination to be perfect it is clear that the difficulties in the way of improvement of the honey bee are formidable. Control of parentage, the first essential in any rational animal breeding programme, is extremely difficult in the case of the honey bee under free flying conditions. Natural mating occurs in the air and a chance mating may take place with *any* drone. Natural mating cannot succeed when the parents are enclosed in a confined space.

The establishment of isolated mating stations goes some way towards the difficulty of parentage control in the honey bee but this sytem is far from fool-proof. Theoretically, the technique of instrumental insemination of the queen bee with semen from a known drone gives the complete answer. The establishment of such a technique on a practical basis has been due principally to the work of American scientists.[4]

The apparatus used consists of a binocular microscope fitted with a specially designed holder which accommodates the queen. To this holder are also fitted a microsyringe and tools designed (a) to hold open the anus of the queen, (b) to depress a small piece of vaginal tissue known as the ' valve fold ' and (c) to depress the sting in the sting chamber.

The queen is held in a cylindrical holder through which is directed a gentle flow of carbon dioxide gas in order to anaethetise her.

The selected drones are dropped into a covered dish containing a little chloroform. The chloroform vapour causes a partial eversion of the genetalia, and the subsequent death of the drone. If the body of the drone is now gently squeezed it is possible to draw off the semen from the tip of the penis by means of the microsyringe. It is estimated that about 5 cmm. of semen is adequate for a satisfactory insemination.

With the anus of the queen fully open the microsyringe is introduced and the valve fold depressed, in order to allow the tip of the syringe to enter the oviduct chamber. When the syringe has been emptied it is withdrawn together with the other tools thus allowing the anus to close and the queen, still anaesthetised, is placed with a few anaesthetised workers from her mating nucleus, into an introducing cage of the candy plug type. This cage is returned to the mating nucleus and, in due course, the queen is released and commences egg laying in from 24 to 48 hours.

Clearly, such an operation demands a considerable degree of skill on the part of the operator since the risk of fatally damaging a queen is considerable.

A further difficulty arises in that there is a considerable loss of semen after the insemination which results in the queen losing, rapidly, her fertility and becoming, sooner or later, a drone breeder.

In natural mating the semen is introduced into the vagina and median and lateral oviducts from whence it is taken up into the spermatheca. Loss of semen is avoided because of the closure of the vaginal orifice by a plug of mucus and the tip of the drone genetalia; the so-called ' mating sign '. Once the semen is absorbed into the spermatheca the plug is removed by the worker bees and the queen subsequently commences egg laying. In the virgin state the sprematheca contains a fluid which, on the queen mating, appears to make way for, or absorb the deposited semen. This process requires some time and until it has been completed and the ' mating sign ' removed, egg laying cannot begin.

If a young queen fails to mate within about six weeks after emerging from her cell, this fluid in the spermatheca coagulates thus making it impossible for any future entry of semen. Young queens may well copulate thereafter but they can never become fertile.

According to Laidlaw and Eckert [5] the spermatheca when filled, contains about 5,000,000 spermatozoa: only a few are withdrawn on each occasion when a fertile egg is laid.

Eventual loss of spermatozoa results in a very old queen becoming either a partial or complete drone layer. A single mature drone has about 10,000,000 spermatozoa in his seminal vesicles, more than enough to inseminate any queen under natural conditions. Owing to loss of semen in instrumental insemination several injections, at intervals of about two days may be necessary in order to achieve even temporary fertility in a queen.

There is, thus, no quick or easy way of producing any form of improved honey bee. Indeed it would seem that nature is somewhat rebellious so far as the honey bee is concerned and, in view of this it is doubtful if the production of a so-called ' improved ' bee is at all possible. Nature would seem to take the view that the honey bee, as we have it today is perfect, as a type: in other words its development has reached the ultimate.

In practice, however, it is found that performance between colonies of bees varies, so that the first step in rational bee management is a critical evaluation of individual colony performance. Chance factors being excluded those colonies which do best consistently, should be used for propagation. Only thus can the beekeeper raise the level of colony performance in the apiary.

The main criterion in evaluation is production level. Clearly, a type of bee that gives consistently high yields, relative to its neighbours, automatically possesses such characteristics as vigour, longevity, nectar gathering ability, ease in taking to supers, ability to draw comb, resistance to disease etc.

In addition it may also possess bad temper but unless the bees are absolutely unworkable such a characteristic should be considered highly desirable. Bad temper seems to be associated with high honey yield and since there is some evidence to show that temper is to some extent governed by the male, it is clear that in a breeding programme due attention to the propagation of selected drones must be given. Fig. 4 will make clear the importance of the male when the technique of back-crossing is considered.

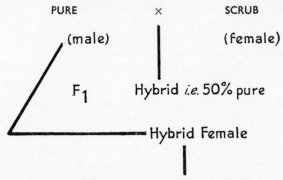

F₂ 75% pure on average but may be entirely scrub or 100% pure

FIG. 4. BACK-CROSS TO MALE

Where one parent, e.g. the male is of the ' pure ' type the technique of back-crossing to the male will, on average give a 75% level of purity but, owing to the random assortment of the chromosomes the F₂ generation may be entirely scrub or 100% pure.

Where one parent, e.g. the male is of the ' pure ' type the technique of back-crossing to the male will, on average, give a 75% purity level but owing to the random assortment of the chromosomes the F2 generation may be entirely scrub or, 100% pure.

Continual systematic selection together with maintenance of colony vigour is the only course open to the practical beekeeper. Maintenance of colony vigour is essential and this can best be achieved by ensuring that the apiary is flooded with selected drones originating from a colony other than that from which the young queen stock has been produced. It is relatively easy to propagate drones in any desired stock and equally easy to suppress their production in any rearing colony.

The larger operator who may be running several apiaries, probably situated some miles apart should select the best in each apiary as his propagating stock. Full vigour in the strain can be ensured by so arranging matters that queens reared in one apiary from one selected colony are mated with drones in one of the other apiaries. In this case drone production can be promoted in the colony from which the breeding material is drawn.

The requisite mating nuclei are best made from colonies in the apiary containing the selected male stock. Each apiary should rear its own selected stock to be crossed with the chosen stock in any other. Thus, with each apiary being systematically requeened the highest level of production will be maintained.

The above noted system is easy to operate: it does not interfere in any way with normal colony management and, above all, it ensures vigour in the strain.

Technique No. 2

QUEEN REARING

Honey bees rear or produce new queens under three well defined impulses:

    (*a*) the swarming impulse,
    (*b*) the supersedure impulse,
    (*c*) the queenless impulse.

No colony of bees will thrive well unless it possesses a first class queen and it is important to realise fully the care taken by the bees in the natural rearing of new queens. The rearing of a queen bee constitutes a unique biological marvel when one considers the effect of the so-called ' royal jelly '. The composition of ' royal jelly ' is complex and although analyses have been made it is recognised that potent substances of unknown nature, which do not show up on analysis, appear to be present in appreciable amounts.

Brood food and royal jelly are glandular secretions derived from the hypopharyngeal and mandibular systems situated in the head of the worker bee. We know that these glands require some time to develop and, that after coming to a peak of activity, they atrophy. Consequently, it is the relatively young bees of the colony, i.e. bees about 7 to 10 days old that are most suited for the production of glandular food.

We also know that there is no difference between a fertile egg laid by the queen and destined to become a worker bee and a similar egg destined to become a queen bee. Further, larvae destined to become worker bees and larvae destined to become queen bees appear to be identical up to the age of 3 days. When the bee colony is rearing worker brood the larvae are, as it were, weaned after about 3 days feeding on pure glandular food but when queens are to be reared the larvae are fed on the full, rich glandular secretion for the entire larval period of about 5 days. As far as is known it is simply the additional feeding of the larvae that gives rise to a completely different differentiation of the tissues in the developing insect.

Both queen and worker castes are highly specialised for the tasks they have to perform and although their origin is common their differentiation is complete.

Queen rearing occurs naturally under the swarming and supersedure impulses and there is no doubt that, assuming the colony to be in good condition, these methods give rise to the best queens. The swarming phenomenon usually coincides with the peak of colony development, i.e. at a time when there is a preponderance of young bees capable of secreting vast amounts of glandular food. It is important to note that the number of queen cells reared under the swarming impulse is limited, rarely exceeding 12 and frequently varying from 6 to 10. Where, of course, there has been some interference by the beekeeper and queen cells have been removed or broken down with a view to the prevention of swarming, the number usually increases in proportion to the degree of interference and, sometimes, 30 or more may be counted.

When considering artificial queen rearing it is important to bear this particular point in mind and refrain from the temptation to rear too many queens in the same colony. Where any selected stock makes swarm preparations queen rearing becomes, as it were, automatic, and all that is necessary is to remove and distribute the queen cells as they mature, to prepared mating nuclei.

However it is often found that the colony selected for propagation does not make swarm preparations at all; or it may choose to make such preparations at a time inconvenient to the queen breeder. Again, it may well be necessary to rear several dozen queens and such a number clearly would not be produced under the natural swarming impulse. Consequently some technique of artificial rearing must be used.

Before considering artificial techniques some thought must be given to the supersedure impulse. Supersedure usually takes place either in the early spring or early autumn. It must be stated clearly that the phenomenon of supersedure of the queen bee is unusual: it is the exception rather than the rule. Precisely why bees decide to supersede their queen and why they do not do so regularly may be arguable but it seems fairly certain that one important consideration is egg laying performance. If the egg laying ability of any queen is at all impaired, either through some form of disease or physical injury, the workers take steps to replace her and begin the construction of queen cells. In this case, however, the number of cells rarely exceeds three. One queen cell is usually commenced a day or so before the others and, once the bees have actually hatched out the first queen the other cells are destroyed automatically.

If one should happen to examine a colony at this particular stage the two queens, i.e. mother and daughter, may be found living quite happily side by side. In due course the young queen flies and becomes fertile and, once the workers in the colony are satisfied that their new queen is working well they destroy the old one by the process of ' balling '. Occasionally the two queens may be found laying eggs side by side, and the old one may be tolerated for many weeks. Eventually, however, she disappears from the hive.

It is convenient in apiary management if a colony supersedes its queen in spring for then the possibility of such a stock swarming is ruled out. Any tendency to non-swarming in a type of bee is a characteristic to be propagated. A non-swarming colony if left to its own devices does not, be it noted, go on for ever. Automatic supersedure usually takes place for 4 or 5 years but thereafter the bees appear to lose the incentive to produce a new queen and, once the extant queen fails, the colony perishes. The life span of a non-swarming colony if left alone works out at about 10 years.

It is clear then that advantage cannot be taken of the supersedure impulse in the artificial rearing of queens.

To rear queens at will and at any selected time use must be made of the queenless impulse. The simple experiment may be tried at any time during the active bee season, of merely removing the queen from a colony. Within a matter of minutes the bees realise their queenless state and something like a mild panic arises. After some hours this panic gradually subsides and the bees quickly begin to restore the situation by the commencement of queen cell construction. Since an emergency has been created the time factor is important and larvae about 3 days old are selected to become future queens.

Such larvae are of course to be found in worker cells and, in fact, the cells are enlarged in order to accommodate the larger larvae which will be produced. Emergency cells can always be recognised since they stick out, like fingers, from the surface of the comb and do not hang down freely as is the case when natural swarm cells are built. Examination shows that such cells are smaller than swarm cells and that they are usually sparsely furnished with royal jelly. Further, anything from 20 to 30 cells may be made according to the strength of the colony. The value of queens reared in this crude manner varies according to their degree of feeding but, provided the larvae have been well nourished even in improvised worker/queen cells, they will subsequently, as queen bees, give a reasonably good performance.

Prime quality queens can be reared under the queenless impulse provided (a) the selected rearing colony is strong in young, nurse bees and (b) a limited number of cells is reared. It is important to realise that, unless environmental conditions are exceptionally favourable, a circumstance rarely encountered in the climate of the British Isles, the number of queens that may be reared and fed properly during the larval stage, at any one time is limited. In practice, if really vigorous stock is to be produced, this means that any rearing colony should be asked to complete no more than 12 cells. Limiting the number means that each larva is adequately tended and receives a surfeit of royal jelly. It is this fact that forms the basis of good quality queens, capable of giving a sustained performance even under the frequently encountered adverse weather conditions experienced in all regions of Great Britain.

Before commencing queen rearing the over-all plan of operation must be considered: this involves the following:

(a) selection of the breeding stock which it is desired to propagate.

(b) selection of a suitable colony to carry out the actual rearing of the queens.

(c) selection of method, i.e. cell grafting, cell punching, etc.

(d) provision of suitable mating nuclei.

(e) care and distribution of queen cells.

(f) choice of suitable time during the active season for queen rearing operations.

The time of year selected will, of course, depend on local conditions and geographical situation but in most regions the choice will lie during the period mid-June to mid-July. At this time conditions are favourable (*a*) for nectar secretion, (*b*) drone flight, (*c*) establishment of nuclei and (*d*) queen mating flight.

Methods

In raising queen cells artificially, use is made of the queenless impulse. Only two techniques will be described here; (*a*) cell punching and (*b*) cell grafting. Both are straightforward and certain in their results.

For the cell punching method a punch will be required (Fig. 5). This consists of a piece of metal tube of 10 mm. inside diameter and approximately 8 cm. in length. One end must have the edge sharpened to facilitate the cutting or punching action. About 5 to 7 days before the date selected for the start of the queen raising operation a frame of unwired wax foundation is placed in the centre of the brood nest of the colony which is to be propagated. If there is no nectar flow owing to inclement weather or other cause the colony should be fed on dilute sugar syrup.

It is much easier to handle breeding material, i.e. larvae, in newly built combs than in old, tough material, although it is by no means essential to use freshly made combs. An empty brood frame with a bar fitted across the centre is also required. This bar should be made to turn round along its axis for ease in fixing the cells.

About 6 cells can be fitted to the under side of the top bar and 6 to the underside of the middle bar.

Two days or so after the 'breeding material' frame, i.e. the frame fitted with the unwired wax foundation, has been given to the breeder colony it should be examined to assess progress in comb building and egg laying. All being well the comb should be almost fully built and the queen should have begun to lay in some of the cells. In practice however, it is sometimes found that queens are slow to begin egg laying in the new comb in which case it is necessary to wait until the comb *has* been used. After another three days the comb should be examined again and the presence of newly hatched and/or very young larvae verified. If such young larvae are present then the cells can be punched out and given to the rearing colony or colonies, as soon as these have been prepared.

Any colony can be used to carry out the actual rearing of the queens provided it is strong in young nurse bees. A minimum standard is that of a stock covering fully 10 or 11 British Standard frames or the equivalent in other denominations. The rearing colony must be dequeened and as much as possible of the young brood removed. The queen may temporarily be established in a nucleus hive but while the young brood must be removed it is important to make sure that no young bees are transferred. All the bees should be shaken and/or brushed from the combs so that they are retained in the rearing stock. This may mean that 3 or 4 frames have to be removed in addition to the queen. The remaining frames should be spaced out so as to leave a space in the centre to accommodate the frame with the punched cells. It is best to maintain this colony in the queenless and virtually broodless state (although of course there will be sealed and hatching brood present but practically no young brood) for from 12 to 24 hours. This gives the bees time to realise fully their queenless condition and makes them reasonably ready to accept the punched cells. After 24 hours, if they have begun cells on any young larvae inadvertently left behind, such cells may now be destroyed.

The comb containing the breeding material can now be withdrawn from the breeder colony, the bees carefully shaken or brushed off and the larvae selected for punching.

While the whole operation may be performed out of doors it is better to do the actual punching indoors at the window of a house or shed where there is a good light.

Fairly young larvae should be selected and the classic yardstick is that they should be of the size of a lettuce seed. At any rate they must be easily seen for if too small they may well be cleaned out by the bees when they examine the cells. The cell punch is oriented over the selected cell and pushed through the comb. With new comb it goes through very easily. A pencil or glass rod is inserted and the cell pushed through the punch. The larvae in the cells should be examined to make sure that they are really floating in their bath of bee milk. If not, then find some that are. The squashed end of the cell is now fixed to the under-side of the holding bar in the frame, by means of some molten wax. A small tin set in a water bath over a spirit lamp or any suitable heating device forms a convenient reservoir of wax. The un-damaged end of the cell containing the young worker larva is now opened out slightly into something like a bell shape but there is no need to overdo this as the bees, when they get busy, further enlarge the cell mouth. This frame is now placed in the centre of the rearing colony, but the flanking frames are not brought completely together, a space of about one quarter of an inch is left on either side. This is to allow ample space for the bees to cluster when building the cells.

Unless there is a really good nectar flow the rearing colony must be fed during the time when the cells are being built. It is advisable to examine the cells about 24 hours or so after they have been given to make certain that they have been accepted. If they have not then replacements must be given. The prepared comb, containing the breeding material is, of course, returned to the breeder colony and is available for further use.

If all goes according to plan, and in practical as opposed to theoretical beekeeping it may not, the cells will be nearing the sealing stage in about 7 days or so. These cells may be left to be finished in the rearing colony as indicated, but it is possible, once they are well started, to have them finished in any other strong, queenright colony. To achieve this the cells can be placed in the top brood chamber of a two- or more storey stock but they must be well separated from the normal brood nest either by a queen excluder or supers or both.

Once the cells are sealed they can be distributed to mating nuclei if such nuclei are immediately available or they can be held until required in nursery cages placed in any convenient colony.

When the work of the rearing colony is completed, i.e. after rearing the dozen or so cells, its queen can be returned. There-after its management will be in accordance with the system practised by the individual apiarist concerned.

Special nursery cages can be bought but my adaptation of the queen mailing cage (Fig. 6), is very convenient whether for

FIGS 5. and 7. QUEEN REARING TOOLS

The lower illustration (Fig. 5) shows the metal cell punch and the upper (Fig. 7) the wooden cell cup former.

FIG. 6. A standard Langstroth deep frame adapted as a queen nursery frame. Standard queen mailing cages may be used as nursery cages if a shallow recess is cut out of one of the partitions to accommodate the queen cell as shown.

temporary incarceration of queens or subsequent introduction purposes.

The developing queen inside the cell is relatively fragile and so queen cells must be handled with great care. Cells are so designed that they hang vertically, with the developing queen oriented head downwards. Queen cells must be maintained in such a way that the queen pupa remains in this position, otherwise there is a grave risk that she will perish. If cells are to be transported any distance, precautions against their becoming chilled must be taken. An insulated box with a hot water bottle as a source of heat is quite satisfactory and easily improvised. The cells, of course, must not be placed too close to the bottle.

Queen cells can, again, be hatched in an incubator but such a gadget is not readily available or indeed workable in, say, an out apiary where queens may well be reared: and there is also the difficulty of feeding and watering the young queens once they hatch. By placing the nursery cages in any suitable colony all that is necessary for the incubation and subsequent maintenance of the queens is already organised by the bees in a very much better fashion than it could be by any beekeeper.

Naturally it is not advisable to keep emerged virgins in nursery cages any longer than is necessary but on occasions they may be retained for 7 to 10 days without coming to any harm. If they are kept for a longer period the bees in the hive in which they are housed gradually cease to care for them and they die from starvation. It is a curious feature of bee life that any queen, old or young, when protected by some form of cage will be tended and fed carefully by strange bees for some days although if such queens were to be released among their caretakers they would be killed instantly.

Perhaps the only advantage of the cell punching method is that the larvae are not physically handled during the operation and so such a method is suitable for the more heavy handed beekeeper. On the other hand, because of the cramped space around the larvae there is the possibility that a certain amount of restriction of growth may take place. First class queens are, however, reared by this method so that this objection is largely theoretical.

B

Cell grafting

The cell grafting technique is that most widely used in the queen rearing industry and, compared with the cell punching technique it calls for a little more skill in operation.

Precisely the same drill is followed as before in the preparation of the rearing material although larvae may easily be grafted from any comb, old or new.

In this system wax cell cups must be prepared beforehand and it is preferable to prepare them just before use so that the wax has a fine, fresh aroma. A quantity of wax is melted in a container contained in a water bath and the cups are formed on a wooden former called a mandril. These gadgets can easily be purchased from any appliance dealer and consist of a piece of wood turned to a diameter of about 9 mm. It is useful to have on hand a beaker or jar (honey jar) of cold water.

The mandril is first of all dipped into the cold water jar and the surplus water shaken off. Next it is dipped into the molten wax to a depth of about $\frac{1}{4}$ inch then withdrawn. The film of wax rapidly cools but this can be hastened by dipping the mandril again into the cold water. At the second dipping into the molten wax the mandril is not allowed to go so far so that gradually, when the operation is repeated three or four times, there is formed a cup which is thicker at the base than at the edges. The whole process takes only a minute or so then the cup is carefully removed from the mandril. A little practice soon determines the correct amount of water to apply as a lubricant on the mandril and it will be found that cups are best removed by a slight twisting action (Fig. 7).

When the requisite number of cups has been prepared they are fastened to the undersides of the top and centre bars of the cell holding frame by means of molten wax taken from the wax container. Alternatively cups may be placed into wooden cell bases. These bases are usually provided with a spike so that they can be fixed easily to the frame.

The next step involves the transference of the larvae from the comb in the breeder colony to the artificially made cell cups. The rearing material is again removed from the breeder hive and the tiny larvae removed from their cells and placed at the base of the cell cup by means of a grafting tool. A sharpened quill serves very well as a grafting tool but since this is not an expensive item of equipment it is as well to buy a specially prepared tool from a bee appliance dealer. If the comb from which the larvae are being selected is new the work can be made easier and more certain by cutting down the level of the cells by means of a sharp knife which has been warmed in the flame of a spirit lamp. This arrangement makes it much more convenient to pick up the small larvae on the tip of the grafting tool and deposit them in the cell cups.

Larvae that are, again, literally floating in their baths of larval food should be chosen so that it is not necessary to prime the cells with royal jelly. The prepared frame is now placed in the centre of the specially organised rearing colony, as in the cell punching method, the hive closed and a feeder given unless there is a heavy honey flow in progress.

As before, the progress of the cells should be watched and if necessary, any rejected ones replaced. After sealing, the cells are easily detached from the frame by means of a pen-knife and can be placed in nursery cages until required or introduced directly to mating nuclei.

The rearing colony is subsequently requeened and restored to normal.

Formation of mating nuclei

Mating nuclei must be carefully made and equally carefully tended. There is a tendency among queen breeders to organise what are known as baby nuclei, i.e. very small bee units. Undoubtedly these are economical in bees and material but mating nuclei which are very tiny lead to absconding bees and queens: in addition they fall an easy prey to predatorially inclined strong stocks.

The ideal mating nucleus consists of three British Standard frames or two Langstroth; or any formation of the equivalent area. At a pinch the mating nucleus may be reduced to two British Standard frames but this minimum should be regarded as the exception. The three frames in the case of British Standard equipment should be organised as follows:

(a) one should contain mostly stores of honey and pollen.

(b) one should contain a small area of hatching brood.

(c) one should contain a small area of brood in all stages.

As a rule it is fairly easy to satisfy these requirements.

Two of the three frames should be well covered with bees in order to minimise possible desertions. Nuclei should be made up either in the late afternoon or early evening so that the possibility of robbing is reduced to a minimum. When made up the nuclei should be transported to another site, at least 3 miles away so that the bees, when released, reorient themselves and there is no depletion of population due to desertion.

Once set down in the apiary selected for mating purposes the queen cells can be distributed. It is always advisable to place the queen cells inside cell protectors so that there is no danger of their being torn down due to recalcitrant behaviour of any bees in the nucleus.

Depending on weather conditions, the young queens may become fertile in anything from 7 to 21 days but the sooner a queen is mated the better. Any queen that has taken some time to mate usually gives a disappointing performance. The time limit for queen mating is about 6 weeks and if a virgin has not become fertile by that time she becomes a drone breeder: as such she is useless.

The queen, once fertile and laying, should be given a trial run of about 10 to 14 days before being introduced to requeen any stock. This will allow an assessment to be made of her pattern of egg laying which must be quite regular with no cells missed out.

In spite of ideas to the contrary, practical experience indicates that the young queen bee mates only once during her lifetime. If, as may sometimes happen, her first copulation has not been fully accomplished she will, most certainly, fly a second and indeed a third time until she has been properly fecundated. When complete mating has occurred the returning queen will have, dragging behind her, the tip of the penis of the drone, the ' mating sign '.

I have no evidence at all that after this has taken place any queen makes a subsequent mating flight although some evidence does suggest that up to 7 mating flights can take place. Any observable variation in the appearance of a queen's progeny is due rather to genetical variability than to the presence of semen from more than one drone.

Multiple mating of queen bees

Nevertheless there does seem to be some evidence that the possibility of a young queen honey bee mating more than once can occur.

Some striking data on queen matings have been presented by Alber, Jordan and Ruttner [6] who conducted a series of experiments on the island of Vulcano in Sicily. They observed the mating flights of about 140 queens of three different races and investigated their progeny. Under favourable weather conditions they found that practically all queens tried multiple mating. Double matings were found to be most frequent while three, four and five copulations were also registered. On some occasions several matings were noted during the course of the same afternoon. In general, it was found that queens mated to two different drones produced the expected two types of progeny. When the weather was bad or if there was a lack of drones, about half the queens began egg laying after the first successful mating flight. The remainder appeared not to be satisfied and continued attempts at mating even up to 24 days between first and last copulation. Although it has been asserted in literature cited by Ribbands [7] that a laying queen may mate again, no evidence to support this view was found. Racial variations apparently did not interfere in any way with multiple mating.

Anatomical study of the mating processes in the honey bee has been made by Wyoke and Ruttner [8] who offer some surprising suggestions. These workers were concerned with the ' anatomical structures which make it possible for the queen to mate with several drones on the same flight, in the short space of about 15 minutes '. It is suggested that the mating sign becomes detached from the drone relatively easily and that it is possible for the queen (equally easily) to eject one mating sign after another and be prepared to ' accept ' other drones in fairly quick succession. Wyoke and Ruttner state ' The fact that the queen left with the mating sign can mate again on the same flight was established by the finding of a mating sign close to a copulating pair '. It must be stated that this evidence seems largely ' circumstantial '.

Much more reliable evidence is offered by D. F. Peer [9] who has also been investigating the multiple mating of queen honey bees. The tests made by Peer were conducted under conditions where the genetic nature of the drone population was accurately known and where the proportion of genetically differing drones was also accurately known. These genetical differences were shown by the body colouration—one type of bee having a brown body colour and the other a black body colour. The brown colouration is known as Cordovan (it is a recessive mutation) and the black colouration is designated ' wild type '.

The tested queens were mated at an isolated mating station at a place known as Algonquin Park, Ontario, where there were no bees located within forty miles. This fact was established by prior test matings. The drone population at the mating station was provided by colonies headed by heterozygous Cordovan queens which were known to be producing mutant and wild type drones in a 1:1 ratio.

When fertile, the queens were grouped according to the type of worker they produced. Three classes were defined (1) progeny of both types, (2) progeny of all wild type and (3) progeny of all mutant. It is clear that those queens in class 1 had mated to one or more Cordovan drones, and one or more wild type drones: those in class 2 with one or more wild type drones and those in class 3 with one or more Cordovan drones. The relative frequencies of these 3 types are set out in Tables 1 and 2.

The striking point about Peer's experiment is that, knowing the drone population to be 50% mutant and 50% wild type, it is possible to calculate the relative frequencies with which these three types can occur.

This is done by making use of the binomial distribution where $(x+y)^n = 1$.

If substitutions are made taking $x = $ the probability of mating with a mutant drone, $y = $ the probability of mating with a wild type drone, and $n = $ the number of matings per queen, the calculated frequencies may be set out as in Tables 1 and 2.

It will be seen that on the basis of a queen mating on an average 7 times remarkably close agreement is found between the calculated frequencies and the observed frequencies.

Similar tests were conducted at Ottawa where the drone population was two fifths mutant and three fifths wild type and

TABLE 1

Groupings of Queens		
Number of Queens	Progeny	Relative Frequency
162	Wild type and mutant	0·9878
1	Wild type only	0·0061
1	Mutant only	0·0061

Known drone population half mutant/half wild type: assumed matings seven.

Number of Queens	Progeny	Expected Frequency
161·44	Wild type and mutant	0·9844
1·28	Wild type only	0·0078
1·28	Mutant only	0·0078

after D. F. Peer.[9]

TABLE 2

Groupings of Queens		
Number of Queens	Progeny	Relative Frequency
293	Wild type and mutant	0·9670
9	Wild type only	0·0297
1	Mutant only	0·0033

Known drone population two fifths mutant/three fifths wild type: assumed matings seven.

Number of Queens	Progeny	Expected Frequency
294·03	Wild type and mutant	0·9704
8·48	Wild type only	0·0280
0·49	Mutant only	0·0016

after D. F. Peer.[9]

again, analysis of the results gave confirmation of the Algonquin Park results.

Making use of the binomial of course assumes that every queen mated the same number of times and that the amounts of semen received and stored in the spermatheca are the same. In the nature of things there would naturally be some variation in these factors: but this method of analysis would seem to be valid.

Technique No. 3

QUEEN APPRAISAL

It is generally accepted that the larger the queen the better her performance; and experience largely suggests that this is so. Queens of course, vary in physical proportions, as happens with all living creatures, and there would seem to be some evidence that this is associated with the circumstances under which the queen is reared. As already indicated, provided that queens are reared in colonies which are strong in young, nurse bees, thus ensuring that the larvae are all well fed, slight variation in the size of adult does not seem to be important.

A useful pointer to the ' goodness ' of a queen may be had if it is possible to examine the queen cell immediately after the virgin has hatched. If this examination shows a surplus of royal jelly still remaining at the base of the cell it may be taken that the queen has been fully fed during her formation and that she will be physically, a fine specimen.

Experience shows that it is the long, slim, streamlined queen that gives the best performance. As queens become older they tend to become more rotund so that some indication of the age of a queen may be had from that aspect of her physical appearance.

There is, of course, only one certain way of telling the age of a queen; that is by marking her in some way according to the year of her birth.

Queen marking may be done in a variety of ways and various marking kits are available from bee appliance dealers. Queens may also be marked by clipping the wings according to a pre-determined code, but this technique has the disadvantage that the queen may, in rough hands, be subject to injury. The simplest and best way is to use brushing cellulose paint, readily obtainable from most hardware stores. The paint may be applied with a fine brush which, while easy to use, may not always be at hand and, most important, must be cleaned immediately after use. It is simpler to use the non-business end of a match: such is always available in the apiary and does not require cleaning afterwards. The technique of marking with paint is simple: the queen is picked up from the comb by means of the thumb and forefinger of the right hand and transferred to the thumb and forefinger of the left hand where she is held by the thorax. A queen may be handled only by the wings or the thorax if she is not to be damaged. A tiny spot of paint is then taken up on the end of a match stick and carefully applied to the dorsal surface of the thorax.

The paint dries almost immediately so that the queen can be replaced on the comb with the minimum of disturbance to the bees. The colour given denotes the queen's year of birth and an international set of colours has been adopted in Europe (Fig. 8).

FIG. 8

QUEEN MARKING COLOURS

Year ending 1 or 6	WHITE
Year ending 2 or 7	YELLOW
Year ending 3 or 8	RED
Year ending 4 or 9	GREEN
Year ending 5 or 0	BLUE

Irrespective of all other factors the efficiency of a queen must be judged by her egg laying ability. In estimating the performance of any queen it is assumed, of course, that she has adequate 'support' from her workers and that her colony is, in every respect, normal. This point is important since no matter how good a queen may be, if she is housed in an indifferent colony she cannot work any faster than the economy of the colony will allow. Apart from this, quite a fair estimate of vigour in a queen may be had by noting her egg laying pattern. This should be more or less continuous and should present a relatively unbroken surface.

Where there has been a recent hatch of young bees the cells should be reoccupied with eggs almost as soon as they are vacated by the adult bees. This condition applies only during the build up and peak period of egg laying: once contraction of the brood nest has begun (normally towards the end of July or early August) the queen will not automatically relay all the cells as they become vacant.

It is not easy to determine accurately the rate of egg laying of a queen bee but a good approximation may be obtained by using the following method. It should be noted that once contraction of the brood nest has begun in the autumn this method loses some of its accuracy.

Determination of egg-laying rates of queen bees

1. The approximate rate of egg laying extending over a period of 3 weeks may be determined by measuring the total area of comb occupied by brood in all stages.

2. The pattern of egg laying on the comb takes the form of an ellipse so that by measuring the length and breadth of the brood area on each comb, the total area, in square inches may be determined. Knowing the total area occupied by brood, the total number of cells (estimated on a basis of 25 per square inch) can be calculated. This figure divided by 21, the average time taken for the development of a worker bee from egg to adult, gives the average rate of laying, covering a 3 weekly period ending at the date of the examination.

The formula may be stated thus:

$$\text{Rate of Laying} = L \times B \times \frac{\pi}{4} \times \frac{25}{21}$$

Where L = length of brood area and
B = breadth of brood area.

3. Each brood area per comb should be computed separately and to facilitate the estimation use should be made of the ' Rate of Laying Table ' given in Fig. 9.

Example calculation

Colony Data. Bees covering 8 combs, brood on 5 combs. Queen reared 1961 Marked white. Adequate stores of honey and pollen. Date of Examination 22:4:1962.
Brood Comb No. 1. Brood present on both sides.
Measurement Side 1. 8×6 inches 48 sq. ins.
  „   Side 2. 8×6 inches 48 sq. ins.

FIG. 9

RATE OF LAYING TABLE

L. × B.	Laying Rate Factor	L. × B.	Laying Rate Factor	L. × B.	Laying Rate Factor
100	94	400	376	710	670
110	104	410	385	720	678
120	113	420	395	730	690
130	122	430	405	740	700
140	132	440	415	750	709
150	141	450	424	760	716
160	151	460	433	770	725
170	160	470	442	780	732
180	169	480	450	790	742
190	179	490	460	800	751
200	189	500	470	810	760
210	198	510	480	820	770
220	207	520	488	830	780
230	216	530	498	840	790
240	226	540	508	850	800
250	235	550	516	860	810
260	245	560	526	870	819
270	254	570	536	880	830
280	264	580	545	890	839
290	273	590	554	900	849
300	282	600	564	910	860
310	292	610	575	920	868
320	301	620	582	930	875
330	310	630	592	940	883
340	319	640	601	950	891
350	329	650	610	960	900
360	339	660	620	970	910
370	348	670	630	980	920
380	357	680	640	990	930
390	366	690	650	1000	940
		700	660		

From the Rate of Laying table the value 48 is equivalent to a rate factor of 45. Using the Table set down the 'factors' corresponding to each comb as follows:

	L	B	L×B	Factor
1st Brood Comb	8	6	48	45
	8	6	48	45
2nd Brood Comb	9	7	63	59·2
	9	7	63	59·2

	L	B	L×B	Factor
3rd Brood Comb	10	7	70	66
	10	7	70	66
4th Brood Comb	10	7	70	66
	10	7	70	66
5th Brood Comb	7	5	35	32·9
	7	5	35	32·9
				538·2

The Rate of Laying is obtained by adding the Factors: e.g. in the above this comes to 538 (approx.) eggs per day over a 3 weekly period ending 22nd April, 1962.

Frequently it is found that virtually the same comb area is occupied by brood in all stages on both sides of the comb: but as this is not invariably so it is best to measure both sides.

This method is simple and no special equipment is required. Measurement can easily be made using an ordinary foot rule, always handy in the apiary, and the figures can be noted in the apiary record book if such is kept.

It is difficult to state precisely what the performance of any queen should be at any given time, but as a rough guide the following rates throughout the year should prove useful.

Month	Daily Rate of Egg Laying
January	Nil.
February	100
March	300
April	500 to 700
May	800 to 1000
June	1200
July	1500
August	800
September	600
October	300
November and December	Nil.

The months of November, December and January can be considered ' rest ' months for the queen and, if brood rearing does take place during that period it can be taken that there is some disturbing factor present, e.g. acarine disease infestation.

The presence of such disease causes irritation among the bees in the colony: this in turn leads to a rise in the temperature of the stock and this false heat induces brood rearing. Such brood rearing necessitates the consumption of excessive stores, relative to the time of year, and, since opportunities for cleansing flights during winter are few, signs of distress and dysentery may appear.

Technique No. 4

QUEEN INTRODUCTION

Many ideas and many methods of queen introduction are current but here it is proposed to give only two: both are safe and simple.

Up to a point and, under certain conditions, bees are able to recognise their own queen and to detect the introduction of a strange one to their colony. The precise mechanism by which queens are recognised by their workers, is not clearly understood and while many theories exist, it is not easy to obtain a complete and objection free fit to the facts in every case. It does seem certain, however, that the behaviour of a queen introduced into a strange colony has quite a lot to do with the reaction of the bees to her presence. If a queen exhibits any uncertainty or ir-regularity in her movements when introduced into a strange hive, in other words if she shows any sign of panic, she is immediately set upon and balled. On the other hand, if the queen is not able to make any sort of rapid movement, e.g. if she has been im-mobilised by immersion in honey before introduction, the bees as a rule lick her clean and then tend her as if she had been the 'mother' of the hive all along: that is assuming the bees to which she is introduced are queenless. Immobilisation techniques are not really foolproof. While a queen may well be accepted she is frequently superseded soon afterwards. It may be that there is also some type of scent associated with every queen, a scent peculiar to her own hive, and this scent may be detected as 'foreign' if the queen is introduced to another stock. If this is so, it is difficult to account for the fact that during a honey flow, or in the evening, during the active season, the laying queen of one colony may be exchanged for the laying queen of another provided an immediate change over is made. Such methods of introduction are best considered as, 'tricks'.

It has already been noted that bees of any hive will feed and care for strange queens provided such queens are protected by

31

means of a cage of wire gauze or perforated zinc. For the safe
introduction of a queen, either with or without her attendant
bees some form of temporary caging is necessary.

As a rule, it is easier to introduce a new queen to a colony
either in spring or during summer, than in the autumn. At the
end of the season, bees are naturally on the defensive and are not
willing to tolerate any disturbance to the organisation of the
colony such as is necessarily involved in queen introduction.

At the risk of pointing out the obvious it must be taken that
the colony to be requeened is, in fact, at the time of the operation,
queenless. It is also equally important to take into consideration
the length of time the colony has been queenless before the
introduction of the new queen. Stocks of bees vary in the speed
with which they react to the loss of their queen: some may begin
to construct emergency cells within a matter of hours while others
may delay a day or more.

If it is a case of straightforward requeening the fact that the
bees will have ample material out of which they can make emergency cells must not be overlooked. In this instance it is better
to avoid any interval between dequeening and requeening so that
the bees will have no inducement to set about the construction
of emergency cells. Where a colony has been queenless for
some time, e.g. weeks or perhaps months, the bees will, in all
probability have become either active or potential laying workers.
Under these circumstances queen introduction becomes difficult,
although by no means impossible. In other words the colony to
be requeened must be in proper condition to receive the new queen.
Similarly, the queen to be introduced must also be in proper
condition if her acceptance by the bees is to be permanent. The
queen should be in laying condition before any attempt is made
at introduction. This rule should be applied irrespective of the
method of introduction used.

If the queen has been reared in the apiary it is assumed that
she will be laying normally in her mating nucleus and that her
performance has been evaluated before introduction is considered.
In this case the conditions for her satisfactory acceptance are
fulfilled.

A laying queen is best introduced by means of a cage and the
' Worth ' cage (Fig. 10) is recommended. One great advantage

a) shows the queen cage with closing block inserted for use when a queen is to be confined within the brood chamber.

b) shows the queen cage with the closing block removed. The opening so made can be temporarily closed with tissue paper or a lightly rolled leaf when the cage is used for queen introduction.

FIG. 10. 'WORTH' QUEEN CAGE

of this cage is that owing to its small size it can be slipped between the combs when in use and the arrangement of the brood nest is not upset. The 'Worth' cage has two openings: one gives completely free access to the cage (this is the one that is temporarily plugged) and the other is fitted with a 'queen excluder'. The excluder takes the form of a staple having an internal measurement of 4 mm.

The queen to be introduced is taken from her nucleus, either alone or with attendant bees, and transferred to the cage.

One opening is plugged with crystallised honey or a plug may be made of soft paper, lightly rolled up to fit the opening: even a soft rolled up leaf may be used. The cage is then slipped between two combs in the brood chamber of the hive to be requeened and, in a relatively short period of time the bees eat away the plug and release the queen. A useful point to note with this technique is that the bees of the colony are able to enter the cage immediately and make direct physical contact with the queen. Since, of course, the queen cannot emerge from this opening due to the excluder staple the necessary delay in the general release of the queen is achieved. The fact that there is no protracted delay in the release of the queen means that she is able to carry on egg laying normally thus ensuring complete and permanent acceptance by the bees. After a day or so the cage may be removed.

Virgin queens may be introduced satisfactorily by this cage technique and provided the virgin is normal and has not been damaged in any way, no difficulty should be experienced in her introduction and permanent acceptance.

If, for any reason, a laying queen has been confined to a cage for a day or two, e.g. when being sent through the mail in a mailing cage, she will be 'off lay' and out of condition. Perusal of the directions for introduction, as set out on the reverse side of the label of the mailing cage, will indicate that this cage may be used for the introduction of the queen, but it is not wise to introduce a queen in a mailing cage directly into a colony of normal strength. After introduction such a queen usually takes about a week or so to come back to full lay and it is in this interval of time that the bees decide she is not up to standard and commence supersedure cells. Such cells may subsequently be

c

destroyed but a definite risk exists that they may not and the newly introduced queen will, in due course, be killed.

On the other hand it is quite satisfactory to use the mailing cage provided the queen is introduced to a nucleus colony of no more than three British Standard frames or the equivalent. Such a nucleus will normally contain mostly young bees and, in the course of a day or so, by which time the new queen will be released, the small group will accept her happily since they are not expecting, nor are they capable of sustaining, anything like the normal output from the queen.

In such a nucleus a fresh, compact brood nest will be established in about 14 days and the position now is similar to that of the newly fertile queen in the mating nucleus.

The queen may now be safely introduced by means of the ' Worth ' cage, or the nucleus may be ' united ', complete, to the colony it is desired to requeen. Uniting may be done either by means of the ' newspaper ' method or by flouring the bees but it is important to wait until evening before carrying out uniting by either method.

Technique No. 5

SWARM CONTROL

In beekeeping practice, swarm control measures have taxed the ingenuity of apiarists for many years. As a result, a host of methods is available but for many reasons surprisingly few are regularly practised by beekeepers. This is due mainly to the fact that they are either complicated to carry out, or that the labour involved is great, and the disturbance to the colony as a result of the manipulation, considerable.

A satisfactory system of swarm control is, however, vital if out-apiary work is to be prosecuted successfully.

In natural swarming the bee colony divides so that a completely new unit may be established and provision made for the renewal of the queen. Thus, the natural swarm wishes to set up an entirely new brood nest where new combs may be built and a new environment exploited. Those bees that remain in the parent stock experience a prolonged hiatus in brood rearing and have the task of carrying the colony along until such time as it is headed by a new queen. While several after-swarms or casts may issue from a colony such happenings are considered bad beekeeping practice. The only redeeming feature of this aspect of bee behaviour is that several young and vigorous queens are produced.

Most swarm control systems aim at thwarting the swarming instinct by such methods as the removal of queen cells: dequeening and requeening: artificial swarming, etc. Any or all of these tricks may be successful but none represents the ideal solution to the problem.

The following technique has been found to be entirely successful and follows, as closely as it is possible to get, the natural trend of the colony at swarming time. It is (*a*) easy to operate, (*b*) requires the minimum of equipment, (*c*) causes virtually no disturbance to the colony, (*d*) maintains the unity of the stock, (*e*) makes provision for the renewal of the queen and (*f*) is equally successful no matter how erratic weather conditions may prove.

For greatest efficiency colonies should be operated in single brood chambers: the Langstroth or Commercial patterns are ideal for general work. The system will, of course, work with any type of hive but where a double brood chamber plan is used extra labour (which means time) is involved.

Method

Phase 1 (Fig. 11). Colonies are allowed to build up normally, stimulation being given as and when necessary and, once the bees are occupying the brood chamber fully, the stock is supered above a queen excluder. Provided a clear brood nest is maintained and good combs are in use, the normal, and indeed even particularly good queen will have ample egg laying space. According to locality, season, etc., additional supers are given as required. If natural swarming is to be avoided completely it is necessary to examine the brood nest once every 9 to 10 days during the period when swarming is most likely to occur. This will vary with locality from May in the southern part of the country to mid-July in northern latitudes. Experience shows that where no indication of swarming is given it is best to leave the colony to develop under its own momentum.

Phase 2 (Fig. 12). When queen cells, i.e. swarm cells, are found, action will depend on the stage the cells have reached. If they are about to be sealed, i.e. when the larvae will have been fully fed, then the second phase of the system can be set agoing.

If the cells are at the cup or young grub stage it is necessary to wait until such time as they are sealed or about to be sealed if provision for the new queen is being made from the colony being treated.

For this phase a spare brood chamber and a nucleus box are required. In a well organised apiary these items of equipment are always on hand. The colony is now re-arranged as indicated. The queen together with 3 combs of bees is placed in the spare brood chamber: the remaining space is filled with new frames with worker base wax foundation and/or built combs. Two, or at most three combs, with queen cells are placed in the nucleus box and some additional bees are shaken in although this shaking in of

extra bees should not be overdone. The nucleus is then completely closed and subsequently transported to the mating apiary
which, it is assumed, is some 3 miles or more distant: there the
bees are liberated.

On the remaining combs any queen cells found are broken
down and the full complement of combs is made up either with

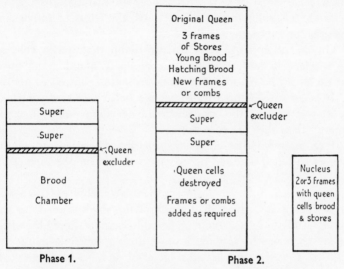

FIGS. 11 and 12. NORMAL COLONY DEVELOPMENT

In phase 1, Fig. 11, the colony is allowed to develop normally
and supered according to prevailing conditions.

In phase 2, Fig. 12, the colony is re-arranged as shown,
provision being made for renewal of the queen by the formation
of a nucleus.

frames with wax foundation or built out combs. The hive is now
re-assembled so that the brood chamber, without the queen, is
placed on the floor. Next come the super or supers, then the
queen excluder and on top of that the brood chamber which
houses the queen.

The position now is that the queen is established in a new
brood nest above a queen excluder, through which she cannot
pass, thus ensuring that no swarm can issue. In this new brood
nest the queen has full opportunity to continue egg laying, and
it will be found that she comes back rapidly to full production.

Prior to swarming, fertile queens reduce considerably their egg output, presumably to make their flight easier when they issue with the swarm. Once the queen comes back to normal the remainder of the bees in the colony feel that the swarming urge has been satisfied, at least temporarily and their effort is now fully directed towards honey storing. In practice it is found that queen cells are so rarely started again in that part of the hive below the excluder that it is not worth the effort of re-checking this area for subsequent cells.

On the other hand it is usually found that queen cells *are* re-commenced in the top brood chamber containing the queen but these can be ignored since they are never allowed to mature.

It is an interesting pattern of bee behaviour that such cells are allowed to reach the stage where the developing queen becomes a pupa: then they are torn down.

It is assumed that adequate provision for honey storage has been given but if not, additional supers should be provided at this stage.

A certain number of drones will, unavoidably be taken with the workers when the first division of the stock is made so that it is advisable to release them on an odd occasion simply by raising the crown board for a minute or so during any fine, flying day. If this is done the drones will soon leave, and any blockage of the excluder by drone carcases is avoided.

Depending on the honey flow, it may be necessary to re-organise some of the combs in the top brood chamber for, if there is a good flow immediately following the Phase 2 move, there may be a tendency for the queen to be crowded out and restricted. Since, however, the brood chamber requiring attention is at the top of the hive and at a convenient height, (assuming the hives are set on low stands on the ground) this check over is neither hard work nor time consuming.

Meanwhile, the young queen in the nucleus hive will mature and hatch from her cell and, depending on the weather conditions will fly and become fertile. It is, of course, unwise to give any set time schedule for this but as a rule the young queen will have emerged and become fertile approximately 3 weeks after Phase 2 was initiated. Until the new queen *is* fertile only an occasional check of the top brood chamber is required.

Phase 3 (Fig. 13). Once the queen in the nucleus colony is laying satisfactorily, Phase 3 of the technique can be put into operation. This consists simply of (*a*) removing the original queen and killing her if she is not required for other duties and (*b*) re-uniting the nucleus, complete with the new queen, to the treated colony. The nucleus can be united complete as indicated or, it is quite feasible and sometimes convenient, according to the

development of the treated colony, merely to introduce the queen by means of the cage method. When re-uniting the nucleus complete with queen, the colony is re-established with the queen and brood nest forming the first brood chamber.

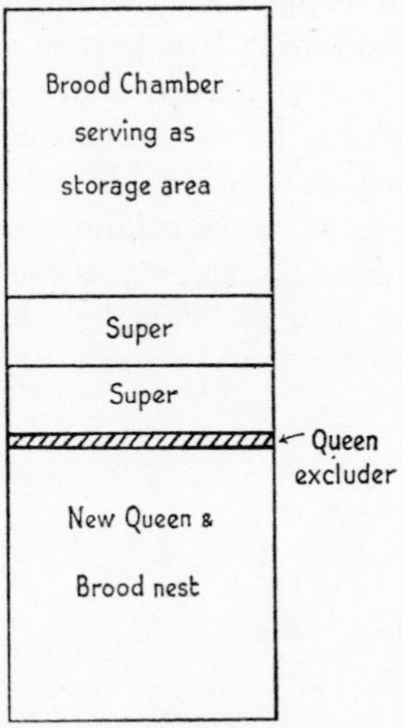

Next come the queen excluder then the supers and what was the bottom brood chamber is now placed on top or utilised in some other way in the apiary until the end of the season.

A colony so treated is prevented from natural swarming but at the same time is never demoralised. Any hiatus in brood rearing is avoided and colony population is maintained at a high level. One

Phase 3.

FIG. 13. In phase 3, the old queen is removed and the new one introduced either with or without the nucleus. The colony is re-arranged as shown.

of nature's objectives under the terms of the swarming act, the provision of a new queen, is achieved, and a colony so organised is in reasonably good fettle if it is to be further exploited on the heather honey flow.

It has been stated that the swarming urge is temporarily satisfied by this technique but it must be remembered that there is *no* way of satisfying this fundamental driving force by artificial techniques. Consequently if a colony is treated along the lines suggested but no provision made for the renewal of the queen, a swarm will issue almost immediately the queen is again free to emerge from the hive even although she may have been incarcerated above the excluder for 6 weeks or more.

The success of the above method depends on the timely renewal of the queen.

Re-queening may, of course, be effected with *any* selected young fertile queen and it is not necessary to wait longer than about 10 days after initiating Phase 2 before de-queening and re-queening. It is best to allow this period of time to elapse so that the excitement of the initial swarming urge may have time to subside below the danger level before a free running queen is allowed to function. It is doubtful if this urge really ever subsides so long as the swarming urge lasts but when the bees realise that they have, in fact, a new young queen, after a period of a few days the impulse to divide the colony subsides and gradually disappears.

Technique No. 6

HONEY PRODUCTION

Successful honey production depends upon the following principal factors:

1. Choice of a suitable forage area or region which offers an abundance of nectar bearing blossom.
2. Colonies of bees suitably balanced so that the greatest possible number of foraging bees is available to take advantage of the main honey flow.
3. The operation of a satisfactory swarm control system.
4. The maintenance of vigorous and healthy stock.
5. Favourable climatic conditions before and during the honey flow.

Forage area and foraging range

It has been shown by Ribbands [7] that the amount of honey produced by a colony of bees is proportional to the distance over which the foraging bee has to operate. This is an extremely important point and it must be given full consideration when apiaries are being established. It is, of course, true that bees can, and do, forage over long distances, but for maximum honey yield the foraging range demanded from the worker bee should not be more than 2000 yards' radius from the hive. In other words the producing colony must be more or less in the geographical centre of the forage area.

The nature and amount of bee flora which may be tapped by bees is, again, vital. Occasional trees or a few acres of blossom, although useful, are not by any means adequate if colony surpluses of 50 pounds and upwards are hoped for. Literally hundreds of trees of good nectar bearing species or, about 2 to 4 acres of clover blossom per colony are necessary if even a modest surplus of about 40 pounds per colony is to be harvested.

The range of nectar producing plants which are of economic

importance to the honey producer is by no means as wide as might be thought. Pollen analyses of honey samples has shown that the most important nectar yielding flowers amount to no more than 19 species (Table 3). This means that the forage area or areas must be carefully reconnoitred and, if necessary, provision made for migratory beekeeping.

Migratory beekeeping

This might seem a simple solution to the problem of adequate forage but there is a limit to the effectiveness of migration. The transportation of bee colonies is a simple, if laborious matter but the physical wear and tear on the foraging force of any colony of bees is a factor which must be appreciated. When bees have been working hard over a period of some days during a honey flow the ' ageing ' of the foraging force is accelerated. If successive flows, at short intervals, are to be exploited, the force of foragers is worn out more rapidly than it can be replaced. This disadvantage is not serious where bees are working successive honey sources at an interval of about 3 weeks, as, for example, such early sources as fruit and/or sycamore followed by clover. On the other hand the flow times of clover, lime, and the beginning of the ling heather may well overlap and when this happens the foraging force is rapidly worn out. Nevertheless all these nectar sources may be exploited successfully by bees and a satisfactory honey surplus obtained. The reckoning, of course, comes later when spent colonies have to withstand a spell of hard weather during the winter. Frequently such worn out colonies show signs of distress and many suffer from dysentery. This condition is often attributed erroneously to heather honey stores or honey-dew admixture in stores when the real cause is a deficiency in vigorous bees. If migration is to be practised, different groups of colonies should be allotted different tasks and it is sound procedure to avoid working any one group on more than one major honey flow. In the end this means more satisfactory wintering and responsive stocks in spring.

Production of bees

If surplus honey is to be produced from any given nectar source the colony of bees must possess an adequate foraging force of workers coincident with the honey flow. Production of an economic force of foraging bees is governed basically by the following factors: satisfactory colony condition in spring: age and/or vigour of the queen: maintenance of efficient combs: provision of a clear brood nest: and a suitable environment which will enable the colony to expand as a result of stimulation either natural or artificial.

Standard winter preparations should ensure a satisfactory colony state in the early part of the year so that the spring population of the colony is adequate to support stimulation of egg production by the queen. In other words provision must be made for the expansion of the brood nest. Environment will, of course, govern the timing of brood nest expansion as well as the method of stimulation whether natural or artificial. In localities where there may be adequate early pollen sources but limited nectar yielding plants the natural nectar deficiency can be made good by feeding sugar syrup. The syrup must be dilute; one part sugar to three parts water, either by weight or volume, otherwise there may be a tendency for the bees to store some of it and so reduce potential egg accommodation space in the brood chamber. There is an added advantage in feeding dilute syrup as in spring, especially when brood rearing gets under way, bees require considerable amounts of water and will often forage for it even under favourable flying conditions. The amount of stimulative feeding required must, of course, be governed by local conditions but it is essential to see that some ' income ' is maintained in the colony during the building up period if there should be any dearth of natural nectar.

The brood chamber, while primarily set aside for the production of brood must also house reserve stores both of honey and pollen. Standard practice indicates that a minimum of 10 to 12 pounds of honey, or substitute stores, is a reasonable reserve for the average colony to maintain during the working season.

The size of the brood chamber must be such that it can accommodate a reserve of honey and pollen as well as providing comb space for the maximum egg output of the queen. The number of eggs likely to be laid by the average queen bee at her peak of production, sometime during June or July, is about 1500 per day, the range being from 1200 to 1700 (see p. 29), but this astonishing output is possible only over a limited period of about 3 weeks.

Relating the foregoing considerations to brood chamber space we find that the equivalent of 13 to 15 British Standard combs, according to comb efficiency, is necessary.

The standardisation of the British comb at a size of $14 \times 8\frac{1}{2}$ inches was unfortunate. If this frame size is used some form of double brood chamber must be adopted. The best solution is to choose either the British Commercial hive, using a frame size of 16×10 inches or the Langstroth hive, using a frame size of $17\frac{5}{8} \times 9\frac{1}{8}$ inches. It should be noted that the outside measurement of the Commercial hive is $18\frac{1}{8}$ inches square which makes a change over from the standard British ' National ' hive a workable project. It is difficult to obtain and even more difficult to maintain perfect brood combs. Normal wear and tear reduces comb efficiency so that a constant watch must be kept on comb condition, and as the area of worker cells becomes smaller, combs must be renewed. Only in this way can the maximum brood nest efficiency be maintained.

In the ' natural ' state bees do not normally make provision for the expansion of their brood area in the most efficient manner possible. Indeed there is a tendency for the actual brood area to be restricted. In the modern beehive where the arrangement of the brood chamber is under the control of the beekeeper, restriction of the brood rearing area can be avoided.

The rule is that at all times during the brood rearing season there should be the equivalent of about one comb of worker cells available as reserve egg laying space in order to cope with any sudden increase of output by the queen.

In districts where there is a surfeit of pollen, bees often tend to hem in and restrict the brood area with so called ' pollen clogged ' combs. These combs should be moved to the flanks of the brood chamber and replaced by empty or nearly empty combs. Alternatively where the colony is in good heart it is sometimes profitable to place such combs directly in the centre of the brood area thus splitting the broodnest. Such ' brood spreading ' may be carried out likewise using empty combs but any form of brood spreading must be done in relation to the strength of the

FIG. 14. Circular honey sections as made in the 'Cobana' plastic section frames.

colony and the prevailing weather conditions. If brood spreading is carried out during cold weather, especially in spring, there is always a risk that the bees will partly re-form the winter cluster and so leave brood exposed to the cold air. Such exposed brood will, of course, die quickly. Chilled brood, when dead, goes black in colour as opposed to the brown colouration of brood which has died from disease.

Provision of adequate brood rearing space may imply the use of a double brood chamber system of management, especially where British Standard equipment is used. While a double brood chamber system is useful it does create extra work and consumes time when, for example, a queen has to be found. It should be noted that queen finding is a usual prerequisite of most swarm control techniques.

Method of honey production

The method of honey production employed will, to a certain extent, determine the size of brood chamber to be used. Comb honey production in the form of the standard $4\frac{1}{4}$ inch square section or the ' Cobana ' circular comb (Fig. 14), is more successful where a smaller brood chamber is used. For best results the brood chamber should be restricted to the equivalent of 12 British Standard combs. Bees do not ' take ' so readily to sections because, when comb building, they are split up into a number of small groups. These small, wax secreting clusters of bees seem to have more difficulty in producing wax than is shown when a larger cluster is able to form, e.g. either on a shallow or deep comb. When a large brood chamber is used in comb honey production there is a tendency for the bees to store honey in the brood chamber rather than in the honey supers. Restriction of the brood chamber, thus forcing the bees to store honey in the sections, usually aggravates the swarming problem. Where surplus honey is obtained in either shallow or deep combs a more natural state of affairs exists and the bees usually respond by giving more surplus honey and less trouble with swarming.

Time of supering

When a honey flow commences it usually builds up rapidly and, over a relatively short period of time, 2 to 4 days, the amount of honey brought in may clog the brood nest if super room is not available. The rule of supering is that as soon as the bees are filling their brood area to capacity the hive should be extended by the addition of a honey super whether or not a honey flow exists at the time. Further, as soon as the bees are working in the first super to the extent of about three quarters of its capacity a second should be given. In extracted honey production it is convenient to place this on top of the first but if sections are being produced the new super should be placed underneath the original super. This will avoid unnecessary travel staining of comb surfaces. Additional supers are given on this principle, as required. In comb honey production it is found, in most seasons and particularly in a difficult season, that a number of sections, especially those at the flanks of the brood chamber, are unfinished. It is well worth the trouble to remove all the completed sections just before the end of the flow and to concentrate all the unfinished ones on the best working colonies. Thus, an uneconomic number of unfinished sections at the end of the season will be avoided.

Foundation v. built out combs

It should be remembered that under the stimulus of a honey flow a certain group of bees in the hive, usually those aged from 16 to 25 days, automatically secrete wax and build comb. Built out combs are, therefore, not a necessary requirement in the production of extracted honey and just as much surplus honey is obtained whether or not built out combs are given. It must of course be admitted that under poor conditions especially early in the season, built out combs are an advantage in obtaining surplus honey. If comb honey is being produced evidence of over production of wax can be had by examining the metal (or plastic) dividers where a number of tiny scales may be detected. Built out combs, if they are stored away ‘ wet ’ in the autumn, are, of course, useful when supering time comes round since they immediately attract many bees away from the brood nest thus relieving congestion at a critical time.

It has for long been the custom to use wired wax foundation for extracting combs. If deep combs are used for honey storage it is certainly best to use wired foundation but where shallows are employed considerable saving may be effected by using extra thin, unwired foundation. Combs built on this foundation are perfectly satisfactory and where a radial extractor is used will give no trouble through breakage. If the extractor is of the tangential type more care will be necessary but if reasonably handled they may also be used successfully in this type of equipment.

Frame staggering

For all practical purposes the standard spacing between brood combs can be taken as $1\frac{1}{2}$ inches, centre to centre. Variation, plus or minus of this value, can, of course, be used and many bee-keepers prefer to use a brood comb spacing of $1\frac{3}{8}$ inches centre to centre.

For comb and extracted honey production a spacing of 2 inches centre to centre, i.e. 'wide' spacing, has come to be standard practice, the advantage of the fatter comb being in evidence when combs come to be uncapped prior to extracting. If the distance between combs is greater than about 2 inches centre to centre the bees will take matters into their own hands and commence building brace comb between them or even entirely new, intermediate combs. When combs are to be built from foundation it is usually best to give ' close ' spacing to begin with; once comb building has commenced the spacing may be extended. An exception to this rule may be made when preparing honey supers for the heather flow. In this case it is in order to give frames with foundation spaced at the wider limit of 2 inches centre to centre. Experience shows that brace comb building or intermediate comb building rarely occurs in heather honey production unless the flow has been inordinately good and prolonged.

Good comb building can, of course, only take place under ideal conditions, i.e. during an intense honey flow. The best place to get first class combs built is in a super immediately above the brood nest.

Honey removal

Where comb honey is being produced it is wise to remove the combs as soon as they are completed, otherwise there is a danger that the ' bloom ' will be taken off the capping as a result of travel staining by the bees continually coming and going across them. In the case of extracted honey production the colour of the comb capping does not matter since cappings will be removed and melted down.

The standard method of honey removal makes use of the ' Porter ' bee escape. This valve device is set in the centre of an escape board (this can be a spare crown board) and the clearing board is simply introduced between the completed honey supers and the space below. After about 24 hours or so, depending on air temperature, all the bees vacate the honey supers which can be removed with the minimum of disturbance to both bees and beekeeper.

Bee escapes must be well maintained and it is vital to see that the small springs are correctly positioned and that they are easily flexed otherwise the bees will not be able to pass through. If, after use, the escape is left on the hive for any time at all the bees tend to propolise the springs to the body of the device thus rendering it useless.

Repellent substances can also be used to drive bees from honey supers. The most commonly used repellent is carbolic acid but this is not to be recommended since, if the acid is strong enough to drive bees from a honey super it is also strong enough to taint the honey. Once honey has taken up the smell of the carbolic it never seems to lose it and is ruined as a table product. A more useful repellent substance is propionic anhydride. This is a colourless liquid, which is mixed with water. It is relatively non-corrosive but should be used with care and not splashed about on the hands or clothing. A special board and fume chamber are necessary. The chemical is given on a pad which is fixed to the underside of the board. A piece of carpet underfelting tacked to a crown board answers well and this is set above an empty shallow super: this forms the fume chamber. A fume dispersal board which consists of a piece of peg board, is set inside the empty super and distanced about 2 inches or so from the top. A bellows arrangement is also necessary (this can be made from an old smoker) to disperse the fumes downwards into the area occupied by the bees. The pad is charged with the chemical and water in the proportions of about 15 cubic centimetres of each, i.e. about a tablespoonful each of chemical and water; the device is set on top of the supers to be cleared and the fumes pumped down into the hive. The bees can be cleared from a shallow super in about one minute.

It is never wise to drive bees from a honey super by means of the smoker. The effect of smoke on bees is to make them run to the honey cells and fill their honey sacks so that many cell cappings will be punctured and the comb appearance spoiled. Honey removal, by whatever method, should be carried out in the evening in order to minimise undue disturbance to colonies and avoid the danger of robbing.

Comb storage

Honey combs must be carefully treated once they have been removed from the hive. Honey is, by nature, hygroscopic, that is, it readily absorbs water vapour from the air and if supers of combs are left about, even for a day in a moist atmosphere, the quality of the honey will suffer. Where comb honey is being produced spoilage will take the form of water exuding from the honey cells; this is the so-called ' weeping ' effect, and in the space of a few weeks such honey, if stored, or if left on the grocer's shelf, will tend to ferment. Section crates should be wrapped in newspaper as soon as possible after they are removed from the hive and stored in a reasonably dry place until such time as they can be cleaned and prepared for market. Again, after cleaning and wrapping, they should be stored until required in cardboard boxes which are in turn well wrapped in newspaper.

The same procedure applies to combs which are to be extracted but it is often more convenient to place them directly into heated cupboards until they can be dealt with. A great degree of heat is not necessary and for a cupboard capacity of 24 cubic feet a small 60 watt tubular heater is adequate.

The use of the queen excluder

It is sometimes considered that the use of the queen excluder reduces the honey harvest because of the fact that it prevents the free movement of bees from the brood chamber to the honey supers. Practical experience shows that if any colony of bees is in good heart and fully capable of storing honey, the queen

D

excluder is in no way a disadvantage. In the production of comb honey it is essential to use a queen excluder if the danger of some brood being reared in the sections is to be averted. Where extracted honey is being produced it is immaterial whether or not an excluder is used since if brood is reared in the honey storage area it simply means that the combs containing it must be left until the autumn or until the brood has hatched and the vacated cells have been filled with honey. It should be noted that honey, extracted from comb that has contained brood is in no way different from honey extracted from virgin comb.

Equally satisfactory results are obtained from 'punched zinc' excluders and rigid wire types. It is of course an advantage for the excluder to have a wooden border since this gives added rigidity and avoids the dislocation of any spacing which would easily allow a queen to pass through. If the zinc pattern is used without a wooden frame it should be handled with a reasonable amount of care and kept flat at all times.

Honey processing equipment

The size and type of processing equipment used will be governed by the extent of the honey production project but quite a large quantity of honey can be handled easily and conveniently with a modest outfit. For general purposes a 20 frame radial honey extractor, power driven by a $\frac{1}{6}$ H.P. electric motor, is satisfactory. An uncapping tray, electrically heated and an uncapping plane, either steam or electrically heated, provide the complete answer to the uncapping and disposal of cappings problem. The molten wax and any honey taken off with the cappings is best run into a pail fitted with a tap at the bottom. Once the wax cools it forms a cake on top of the honey. The honey in the pail can be conveniently run off into the strainer.

The honey extractor can be mounted on a platform high enough to allow the honey to run straight into the strainer of the settling tank or it may be set on a lower platform and the honey run into a pail, which can be easily emptied into the strainer.

It is satisfactory to use a settling tank fitted with a strainer having an effective straining area of 112 sq. ins. The standard honey strainer is fitted with fine wire mesh or perforated zinc and it is an advantage to supplement this with a piece of butter muslin or linen scrim cloth supported on the *inside* of the strainer by means of a stiff wire hoop. If honey is at all cold it will be extremely difficult to strain: also if there is an excess of wax particles present the honey will take a long time to clear the strainer. It is wise to have several straining cloths available and if clogging does take place a clean cloth can be given and the work speeded up.

Several patent strainers are available such as the Ontario Agricultural College pattern. This consists essentially of several wire gauze cylinders of such a size that one fits easily inside the other. The largest mesh is in the centre and the smallest constitutes the final straining area. This is a device which works admirably, but just as efficient results are obtained with the simple strainer which is easily cleaned and cleared from time to time when a large quantity of honey is being handled.

The capacity of the settling tank should be about 2 to $2\frac{1}{2}$ cwts. This size is not too large and is easily handled and cleaned. Many honey production projects are operated by one person so that excessively large and unwieldy equipment is best avoided. By nature, honey is a viscous liquid and its rate of flow is affected by temperature and the lower the temperature the more difficult it is to handle. If any batch of honey contains a large amount of wax particles, straining will take a fairly long time at normal temperatures. If honey is to be pumped from the extractor into settling tanks it must be heated and the pipe line also maintained at a temperature high enough to ensure a satisfactory flow. Where high quality honey is to be produced heating must be avoided or kept to a very low level. Honey will strain quite satisfactorily at a temperature of 90° to 100° F. and at this level there is no possibility of destroying any of its natural goodness. For reasonably speedy working the extracting room temperature should be about 80° to 90° F. The use of an air extractor fan, fitted to a window, will make working in such a warm room quite comfortable. It is also an advantage to coil lengths of electric soil heating cable round the extractor base and round the settling tanks. Soil heating cable can be obtained in convenient lengths of approximately 40 feet with a wattage rating of about 150. This will provide just enough heat to keep the honey at a useful viscosity level and speed up extracting, settling and bottling. Honey should be allowed to settle in the settling tank for 12 to 24 hours but no longer. This period of time is sufficient to allow practically all the air bubbles to come to the top of the tank where they may be skimmed off, as a scum. As soon as the scum has been removed the honey should be transferred to jars, cartons or tins. Since honey is hygroscopic in nature it is not wise to leave it exposed to the air for any length of time since the upper layer in the container will tend to absorb sufficient additional water vapour to allow the multiplication of yeasts, naturally present in any honey. If consideration is not given to this point there is a distinct possibility that some of the honey will subsequently ferment and be completely spoiled.

Honey containers

The first consideration anent any honey container is that it should be airtight. Honey jars, of whatever shape, should be of a screw top pattern and fitted with waxed wads. Tins should have well fitting airtight press-on lids. Tins provide a convenient means of storing honey in bulk but unless special heating facilities are available it is best not to use too large a tin. Twenty-eight pound capacity tins can be accommodated fairly easily in a large pot which can be used as a water bath but the 14 pound size is perhaps the easiest of all sizes to handle. When honey which has crystallised in tins has to be melted down for subsequent bottling it will be found that the larger the tin the longer the time taken for the honey to liquefy and the longer the honey must be subjected to heat. As has been indicated, heating honey is not advisable and where this must be done in order to reconstitute the stored product, the heating should be kept to a minimum.

Liquid honey may also be put up in waxed cartons having either screw or press on lids. It should be remembered, however, that once honey has crystallised in this type of pack it is not possible to reliquefy it by heating and if the crystallisation is at all ' hard ' the honey may be difficult to handle ' on the table '. Waxed cartons are, of course, useful where ' creamed ' honey is being packed.

Various ' novelty ' packs are on the market, one of the most successful being the plastic container shaped in the form of a bear. These plastic containers can withstand heat and so allow honey that has crystallised to be reconstituted without difficulty.

Honey heating cabinet

Crystallised honey can be reliquefied without the use of a water bath if some form of heating cabinet is used. Several patterns of varying capacity are on the market but quite a useful type can be made easily from any large box. A moderate sized cabinet can be fashioned out of a tea chest. The principle involves the use of two boxes, an inner and an outer, spaced about one inch apart with the interspace filled with some insulating material. Newspaper answers well here. The heat can be supplied either by 3 or 4 electric bulbs placed at the bottom of the box and pointing inwards towards the centre or by two 60 watt tubular heaters. The inner box is about 3 inches smaller in height than the outer and may be fitted with 1 or 2 shelves made so that they can be easily removed. The cabinet should also be fitted with a thermostat adjusted to maintain a temperature inside of about 130° F. The larger the box, the larger of course, must be the heating element. Heating honey in such a cabinet is a fairly slow process if the honey is crystallised in large containers but where honey in labelled jars has crystallised the heating cabinet avoids the necessity of relabelling after melting as would have to be done if the water bath technique were used.

Creamed honey

All honey types tend to crystallise sooner or later and many honey consumers prefer their honey in the granulated form. Honey, unfortunately, has a tendency to crystallise in varying degrees of hardness, and sometimes when naturally crystallised, it is so hard that difficulty is experienced in getting it out of the jar when using a spoon. For table use crystallised honey should be of a soft consistency so that it is easily spread. Soft consistency in granulated honey is associated with the size of the grain or crystal formation. Small crystals give a smooth and usually soft texture while large crystals produce a coarse matrix. The texture or grain of the granulation is closely related to the speed with which the honey crystallises: the more rapid the crystallisation the finer the grain. Where it is intended to supply creamed crystallised honey for market it is best to promote the crystallisation artificially by the process known as ' seeding ' the liquid honey with honey already finely granulated. The proportion of granulated honey or ' seed ' to liquid honey is not critical but in practice about 1 pound to a 14 pound pail of liquid is adequate. The liquid honey should have been standing overnight in a temperature of approximately 75° to 80° F. so that it is fairly fluid and workable. In order to promote crystallisation as rapidly as possible the ' seed ' must be incorporated thoroughly throughout the liquid honey either by the simple process of stirring by hand, with a large wooden spoon or similar tool, or better still, by a hand food mixer, electrically operated. If a food mixer is used it must be set to rotate at the slowest possible speed. If the speed is too great many air bubbles will be incorporated and quite a considerable amount of undesirable frothing will result. After the first stirring the honey should be kept at a temperature of about 60° F., i.e. normal room temperature. After an interval of 12 to 24 hours a second stirring should be given and the environmental temperature raised to about 80° F. The degree of crystallisation should then be noted and if it appears to be well advanced the honey should be run into the final containers, i.e. jars, etc. while it is still in the mobile state. This straightforward method normally gives a crystallised honey that is easily spread yet is not too soft in consistency. In addition recourse has not been made to heating the honey in any way.

If honey has crystallised in tins and is of a hard or coarse texture it may be reconstituted to produce a very soft creamy product if the tin is immersed in a water bath (or heating cabinet) until the mass has been almost, but not quite, completely liquefied. The temperature should be kept around 140° F. to avoid undue discolouration of the sample if it is a light coloured honey. At a point when there is left only a thin core of crystallised honey, the tin should be withdrawn from the heat and the honey allowed to cool to a temperature of about 80° F. About a half a pound of ' seed ' per 14 pound tin should now be added and thoroughly incorporated as outlined above. When crystallisation has reached the required degree the honey is run from the settling tank into suitable containers.

Technique No. 7

HEATHER HONEY PRODUCTION

The common ling heather (*Calluna vulgaris*) ranks high as a honey-yielding plant, especially in Scotland. Heather honey is unique in character and is highly valued, so that the heather plant is of considerable importance to the beekeeper.

Many moorland areas offer virtually inexhaustible sources of heather honey but because the ling heather is a late flowering plant and moorland areas are normally remote, thus necessitating the movement of colonies of bees to the foraging region, the production of ling honey presents a variety of problems and demands a special technique.

Locality

In the selection of a suitable locality for heather honey production, attention must be given to the extent of the heather area and age of the plants, the nature of the soil on which the heather is growing and the accessibility of the site chosen for the hives and the available shelter.

Small patches of heather, amounting to a few acres, are of little value to bees; but normally little difficulty presents itself in selecting a really extensive moor. The age of the heather plant is, however, more important than is normally realised. The best yield of honey is obtained from young heather plants growing to a height of 4 to 8 inches. Old heather which has grown rank and has reached the small shrub stage does not seem to produce nectar in any quantity, and it is only under the most favourable conditions that economic quantities of honey may be obtained from such regions. Ideal conditions are realised on moors that are properly managed for grouse shooting, since in such areas regular, controlled burning of the heather is practised. In this way a yearly succession of young heather plants is produced. For best nectar yield, the heather should be growing on the shallowest of soil, indeed almost bare rock. Where the plants are growing in a bog or over a considerable depth of peat, the honey-producing potential is lowered. Height above sea level, on the other hand, does not seem to affect nectar secretion in any way, but at lower altitudes the greater range of flora available to the bees frequently results in a ' blend ' type of honey rather than pure heather honey.

Since hives are normally transported by lorry, van or car trailer, it is an obvious advantage to have a site that is easy of access so that the carrying of hives over long distances is avoided. A certain amount of shelter for the hives is also desirable, for if they are placed in an exposed position many hours of bee work will be lost and a considerable toll taken of the foraging force. If possible, a site half way up the side of an east-west running valley should be chosen, since this offers both north and south facing slopes and thus extends the duration of the honey flow.

Obviously, the further the bee has to fly to the nectar source, the less actual work of honey storage will be done so that it is a *sine qua non* that the hives should be set right in the centre of the heather area, or at any rate in such a position that heather is available within a radius of 1500 to 2000 yards. For maximum efficiency in any form of honey production, the equipment used must be simple. For this reason, and particularly in heather honey production, where in most cases hives have to be transported, the single walled pattern of hive is desirable. Hive design varies considerably but it is a decided advantage to have the floor board cut flush with the brood chamber, so that there is no projection at the front of the hive to catch on anything during handling. In addition it will be found that hives may be packed more easily when they are flush all round. The hive stand should be detachable, again to facilitate stowage and transport. Where hives have to be moved, either in heather work or migratory beekeeping, the self spacing ' Hoffman ' type of frame is the most satisfactory to use. These frames, since they can move only vertically and are not displaced laterally, retain their position, even though a hive may be bumped in transit. Where metal ends are used for frame spacing, lateral movement of the frames is possible: this can, on occasion, cause loss of bees through crushing or undue excitement, due to the rubbing together, and bruising of honey combs in the brood chamber.

Preparation of colonies of bees for the heather honey flow is best carried out between the middle of July and the end of the month, according to the state of the local honey flow. It is sometimes found that a late clover flow or a flow from the lime trees may set back the timetable of heather preparation, but it is important that the heather honey producing stocks should be on the moors as early in the month of August as possible.

The brood chamber

Experience has shown that the heather honey flow is of short duration: at the most it lasts intensively for 10 days but often only for 5 days. Consequently, if the maximum amount of

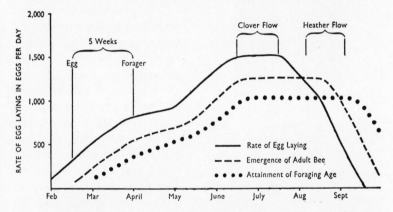

FIG. 15. Graph showing relationship of egg laying to season of year and production of foraging bees for clover and heather honey flows.

surplus honey is to be harvested, the colony must necessarily be strong in foraging bees. Also, owing to the more severe working conditions experienced by the bees at higher altitudes, there is quite a considerable loss of bee life, so that if this effect is to be offset the colony must also contain a considerable potential of new bees in the form of brood. The age of the queen has a direct bearing on this point, since, with any fertile queen over the age of 2 years, there is a marked decrease in egg production from the end of July onwards. The graph (Fig. 15) shows the relationship of egg production to availability of foraging bees for both the clover and heather honey flow. Colonies containing old queens, therefore, may produce quite an amount of honey, but owing to the natural contraction of the brood nest in early autumn an excess of honey will be stored in the brood chamber.

Excess heather honey in the brood chamber, together with limited brood production during August and September, frequently results in unsatisfactory wintering of colonies which have been used for heather honey production. This difficulty may be avoided if some care is taken in the preparation of the colony for the heather flow.

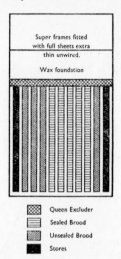

Super frames fitted with full sheets extra thin unwired.

Wax foundation

▨ Queen Excluder

▤ Sealed Brood

▨ Unsealed Brood

■ Stores

FIG. 16. Correct arrangement of combs in brood chamber for heather honey production. The sealed brood occupies the centre area and is flanked by unsealed brood and honey storage combs.

If possible, the queen should be of the current year (introduced to the colony about mid-July or so) but certainly not more than 2 'laying' years old. If necessary the combs in the brood chamber should be rearranged so that in the centre are placed the combs containing sealed brood and on the flanks the combs of unsealed brood, while at either extremity the combs of reserve stores are set (Fig. 16). Normally, the colony should be limited to one brood chamber for heather work, but if two (for example a deep plus a shallow) are used, the above noted comb arrangement still applies. Necessarily, there is a certain amount of constriction of the colony for heather honey production, but if young queens head the stocks the possibility of an August swarm is ruled out.

Since it is possible for bees to experience a considerable period of dearth during their first week or so on the moors a reasonable amount of reserve stores should be ensured to each stock. About 15 to 20 pounds should be considered a safe minimum.

Although the brood nest is contracting during the month of August, it is always safer to use a queen excluder to confine the queen to the brood area of the hive. There is no reliable evidence to suggest that the use of the excluder results in any loss of honey.

Each colony should be provided with two honey supers if shallows are used, or one deep if deep boxes are favoured. If necessary, additional storage space can be given later, but initial restriction is necessary to induce comb building. The spacing of the combs in the supers is not critical and where the bees build their combs from wax foundation, adjustment of spacing, as comb building proceeds, is not necessary.

Methods of honey production

The physical nature of heather honey is such that it cannot be extracted from the comb. Thus, heather honeycomb must either be (a) pressed and the honey subsequently run into jars, (b) scraped to the ' mid-rib ' of the comb and the resulting ' mash ' of honey pressed, or (c) consumed as comb honey.

For pressing, the surplus honey can be produced in deep or shallow combs. Such combs should be built from foundation each time, since new or ' virgin ' comb may be pressed much more efficiently than ' old ' or already built comb. The foundation used should be of the extra thin unwired type. The pressing of heather honey is necessarily, a slow process, but the work may be lightened if a large pattern of honey press is used. The best material to use for wrapping the honeycomb prior to pressing is linen scrim cloth. This is much easier to work with than muslin and will withstand a much greater degree of wear. The honey tray of the press should have a large honey gate with a diameter of at least 2 inches to facilitate bottling.

Some beekeepers employ the practice of scraping the honeycomb to the mid-rib subsequently pressing the scrapings. This method, while saving the cost of new foundation each year, is slow and the extraction level of honey is reduced. An efficient honey press will give an extraction level of approximately 96% leaving only the thinnest of wax wafers in the scrim cloth. This wax, can, of course, subsequently be rendered or melted and traded for new foundation.

It is usual to produce comb honey in the form of the ' section ' and much heather honey is so obtained. However, it is also possible to produce heather honey, owing to its gelatinous nature, in the form of 'cut comb'. Heather honey produced by this method has been found to command a very ready market and has the great advantage of being the most economical method so far devised. In this technique the 'pieces' of comb are cut from the frames, usually by means of a wire, similar to a cheese cutting wire, then wrapped in transparent paper. Comb heather honey so produced can be handled easily, although normal care is necessary if damage to the comb is to be avoided. Another useful method which makes the handling of the 'cut comb' easier is to place the pieces of comb in small waxed cartons such as are used in the confectionery trade and known as 'divi trays'. These trays are cheap and are readily available in sizes which hold 6 and 8 ounces of comb respectively.

The pieces of comb are cut to the required size (make a simple template out of the bottom of a tray), placed in the tray and the whole pack wrapped in cellophane. The packer's label can be incorporated in the wrapping and a most attractive and easily handled, hygienic product is obtained.

Special difficulty is often found when producing sections owing to the fact that bees, under normal honey flow conditions, are loth to build individual small combs. This difficulty may be largely overcome by producing the sections in hanging section frames which are of the same outside size as the shallow frames and so fit conveniently into a shallow box. This point also applies to the production of sections on the clover, or other flows. It is best to place the sections in four hanging section frames in the centre of the shallow box and flank them by shallow frames to complete the comb space. The creation of a 'funnel' effect in the centre of the honey storage area is conducive to comb building in the warm air current thus produced.

Another advantage is that the wood of the sections produced in hanging section frames is kept clean, an important point in marketing.

Mention must also be made of a method of 'extracting' heather honey by means of what is called a honey loosener. Heather honey possesses the property of thixotropy, that is, it is normally in the nature of a gel which will not flow, but if it is stirred or agitated in any way the gel becomes sufficiently liquid to allow it to flow. The honey loosener consists of a ' brush ' of steel needles which are pushed up and down in the comb, thus causing the gel to become temporarily viscous. The ' needled ' combs are then extracted in the normal way. It must be noted, however, that when using this technique the work has to be carried out in a really hot room and a ' tangential ' type of extractor must be used. If good quality ling honey is being handled it is normally possible to remove not more than about 80% from the combs: this is rather too low a level of extraction to be strictly economical. Subsequent straining of the ling honey is slow and difficult unless the honey has been heated. This is a decided disadvantage since owing to the high colloid content of ling heather honey the least heating tends to darken the sample, and may also carmelise it.

A ling heather honey loosening machine of Norwegian origin is now on the market and works reasonably well but the above noted objections to handling ling honey by the loosening technique still apply.

Transporting the colonies

When moving colonies of bees it is important to ensure that (a) the hive parts are secure and that no bees can escape, and (b) the bees have adequate ventilation. The various hive parts in the single wall equipment may be securely fastened by the use of crate staples and this method is recommended above all others (often more elaborate), as it is simple and inexpensive.

A crowded colony of bees may suffocate easily, so that some thought must be given to the question of providing adequate ventilation. Special measures, however, are necessary only when the bees are to be confined during the hottest part of the day. The hive entrance must be kept dark so that excitement among the bees is at a minimum. This means that the entrance requires to be closed completely. This can be done by means of a specially prepared entrance block which can be secured to the front of the hive by means of wood screws. Several ' patent ' hive closing devices are on the market but a most useful and inexpensive closing ' block ' can be made from a strip of foam rubber. This should be fully an inch thick (depending on the depth of the hive entrance) and about an inch or so longer than the entrance is wide. The ' block ' can be pushed in so that it is quite flush with the hive sides and the elasticity of the rubber ensures that it remains firmly in position. An entrance closer of this nature is very easily inserted and removed and has the advantage of being light and easily stowed away.

Ventilation, if necessary, can be provided from the top by means of a screen-board of perforated zinc. Bees are best moved in the early morning, a start being made early enough (according to the distance to be travelled) to allow the bees to be liberated by 9 or 10 a.m. at the latest.

A workable procedure is to close the bees in sometime around 11 p.m. to midnight and load up and move off next morning around 7 a.m. This allows about two hours to travel to the heather site, set down the hives and liberate the bees before 9 a.m. When such an arrangement is possible no special measures regarding ventilation are necessary.

Setting down and liberating the bees

It is recommended that all hive stands should be placed in position and the hives set down before any bees are liberated, thus avoiding unnecessary excitement—this time, of the beekeeper. Under normal circumstances there is always a considerable amount of drifting bees in the apiary, and to minimise this the hives should be set at least 3 feet apart or in groups of 3 or 4, allowing 5 to 10 feet between each group. There is always a tendency to place hives in a long row on the heather stance, but this should be avoided, since it leads to excessive drifting. The opening of the hive door should be synchronised with a good puff of smoke from the smoker, thus avoiding an angry rush of bees from the entrance.

Once set down the hives require little attention during the month but if weather conditions are favourable, provision for additional storage space must be provided.

As a rule there is little the bees can harvest from the heather after the end of the first week of September, and any time thereafter the stocks may be brought back to the home apiary, the honey removed in accordance with the normal technique and processed according to the method favoured.

The nature of ling heather honey

The chief value of ling heather honey lies in its unique flavour and the fact that, unlike other honey types, it is gelatinous and does not flow. It is curious, however, that when freshly gathered and stored, ling honey is very 'watery' and, if a comb is held horizontally, the honey will run out just like water.

The 'goodness' of heather honey may be assessed by the fact of its being gelatinous, so that a piece of honeycomb may be cut without any movement of honey occurring. Heather honey in the jar may be judged for quality by the size of air bubble it contains. These air bubbles are introduced in the process of pressing and, owing to the extreme viscosity of the honey, remain trapped. The larger the air bubble the better the quality of the honey.

In spite of its gelatinous nature, heather honey normally contains water to the extent of 22% to 23% and sometimes more, which probably accounts for the tendency of this honey to ferment.

It is often stated that heather honey does not granulate, but there is little reliable evidence to support this view. It is true, however, that where a really pure sample of ling honey has been obtained, granulation is slow, sometimes taking as long as 2 years to commence. Such crystallisation is characterised by excessively large crystals, which sometimes attain the size of small peas.

The purity of heather honey may also be assessed by pollen analysis. An admixture of nectar from other honey plants may easily be detected and an accurate estimate of the purity, or otherwise, of the honey, made.

'Standards' for pressed ling heather honey

From time to time, 'standards' for honey which is to be offered for sale, have been set down by various interested bodies both official and unofficial but such standards have applied primarily to honeys other than ling heather.

The term 'heather' honey may be interpreted somewhat loosely since both Bell heather (*Erica* sp.) and Ling heather (*Calluna vulgaris*) yield honey of which large surpluses may, under favourable conditions be obtained.

Bell heather honey and Ling heather honey are very different.

Erica honey may be regarded as a normal, liquid honey which ' flows ' and which may be extracted from the combs, using normal extracting techniques. It is dark red in colour often stated to be of a port wine shade, has a pleasant mild flavour and aroma and is, altogether, a fragrant honey. The bell heather plant is, however, limited in its distribution and as a result large quantities of this type of heather honey do not normally appear on the market.

In contrast to bell heather honey, that from the Ling heather is, or should be, of a gelatinous nature (as noted above) thus preventing its extraction from the comb by normal methods. The colour is light amber and the aroma and flavour positively pungent. Another characteristic (again as noted) is the large air bubble: the size of the bubble and the quality of the ling honey being closely related.

In practice it is doubtful if absolutely pure ling heather honey is often obtained. Conditions must be such that at the commencement of the ling flow, hives contain no *honey* stores (they may, and often do, contain fair amounts of sugar syrup stores) and only the *Calluna vulgaris* flower is available to the foraging bees. Such conditions do not often prevail and, in practice, most of the ling heather honey produced is, strictly speaking, not ' pure ' in the true sense of the word.

Concerning the purity of ling heather honey the following from a paper by the late J. Pryce-Jones,[30] entitled ' Rheology of Honey ', is of interest.

'. . . over three hundred samples described as heather honey were examined, the protein content of these samples varying from 0·2% to 1·86%. Pollen analyses indicated that very few of these samples had been derived from heather nectar alone. From various evidences it may be safely assumed that protein content is a criterion of the purity of a sample of heather honey but it is difficult to set a rigid standard. As the samples which contained 1·86% protein contained no pollen grains other than those of heather, this figure has been adopted as a standard for pure heather honey. As pollen analysis showed, samples containing 1·0% or less of protein were mixed with a high proportion of honeys derived from the nectar of other flowers. Pure heather honey remains gelatinous for many years but if the protein content is less than 1·0% crystallisation takes place in a few weeks. If its value is between 1·0% and about 1·5% crystallisation is delayed for many months and the crystals resemble small pin heads which may ultimately grow into spheres 3 or 4 mm. in diameter.'

It is clear that ling heather honey may vary considerably in quality.

In view of this the following five points may be taken into account when assessing the purity of ling heather honey.

1. Pollen analysis should show not less than 60% *Calluna vulgaris*.
2. Protein content should be not less than 1·0%.
3. The suspended air bubble should be approximately 1 mm. in diameter.
4. Colour should be pale amber to amber.
5. Consistency should be such that little or no movement of the honey is observed when the container is tilted (the honey is assumed to be in the non-crystalline state).

Points 1 and 2 of course necessitate laboratory analysis but an approximate, 'on the spot' grading can be made on the basis of points 3, 4 and 5. While these values are suggested as representing a minimum standard, ling heather honeys showing values

TABLE 3

Per cent samples in which pollen occurs

Plant	England	Scotland	Ireland	Wales
Trifolium repens	91·2	93	100	93
Prunus/Pyrus sp.	77·4	47	76	73·3
Rubus sp.	54·1	45·1	36	79·7
Acer sp.	49·8	36·3	40	67
Castanea sp.	47·4	7·8	8	20
Tilia sp.	49·7	20·6	4	33·3
Brassica sp.	52·5	38·2	32	46·6
Ligustrum sp.	33·8	7·8	20	40
Vicia sp.	33·9	24·6	8	6·7
Trifolium pratense	31·8	10·8	20	—
Chamaenerion sp.	22·7	34·2	4	40
Cirsium sp.	23·2	25·5	8	40
Campanula sp.	21·0	10·8	4	13·3
Calluna vulgaris	6·8	41·1	20	6·7
Heracleum type	25·6	18·6	20	13·3
Taraxacum type	25·0	25·5	52	33·3
Centaurea sp.	21·0	13·7	32	13·3
Aesculus sp.	15·9	3·9	—	13·3
Erica sp.	9·3	20·2	4	33·3

E

in excess may command a higher than normal price. On the basis of these suggested standards Grade A ling heather honey would show a pollen content of 100% *Calluna vulgaris*, a protein value of approximately 2%, an air bubble of 2 mm. diameter, amber colour and a consistency of that of a firm jelly.

Perhaps the most important criterion by which to assess the quality of ling heather honey is the protein content, since, if this is high, points 3, 4 and 5 automatically follow. Within the limits of the technique pollen analysis gives a fair indication of the relative proportions of nectar from the various sources which the bees have been working. The water content of ling heather honey is not a satisfactory criterion upon which to fix a standard. Provided the colloid content is about 3% such high moisture values as are found with ling heather honey need cause no worry. Nevertheless, since all honey, and especially ling heather honey, is hygroscopic, it is particularly important to see that it is stored in a dry place both before and after pressing.

Technique No. 8

HONEY JUDGING

The technique of honey judging, apart from the application of a modicum of common-sense, is metaphorically speaking, almost but not quite a matter of taste.

In judging honey it is essential to have before one (*a*) a clearly defined set of standards and (*b*) a technique to make the most efficient use of the standards chosen. A honey judge, knowing precisely where he is going is in a strong position since his word, like the word of all judges, is or ought to be, final.

Normally, preparation has to be made to judge 5 classes of exhibit: these are (1) liquid honey (2) granulated honey (3) comb honey (4) heather honey (5) bees wax. In addition there may also be a class for mead or some product of the culinary art. Suggestions as to the judging of honey cooking will not be attempted here and so far as mead is concerned only tentative points will be made since ideas on mead are inclined to be more emotional than rational.

The honey judge, having set his standards may simply carry them round in his head and go about his task on the ' elimination ' basis. Such a scheme can, and often does, work well enough but it is much more satisfactory to work according to a points system so that a reasonably truthful answer supported by written evidence may be given to some disappointed competitor bold enough to challenge the judge on any of his decisions. The fact that the judge's decision is final does not prevent a competitor lodging an appeal if he feels that his honey has not been properly considered.

The following ' points ' system works well in practice although it must be admitted that where there is a large entry in any class it takes quite some time to complete.

Class : Liquid honey (Fig. 17)

Standards for this class should take note of the following points: (*a*) viscosity or ' body ' of the honey; (*b*) colour and

67

brightness; (c) cleanliness; (d) absence of granulation; (e) flavour and/or aroma.

These headings should be set out as shown in the illustration and an appropriate number of points allotted to each. The number of points given per standard may, of course, vary according to individual emphasis. Viscosity is considered the most important attribute of honey since it gives a definite indication as to

FIG. 17

CLASS: LIQUID

No.	Viscosity	Colour and Brightness	Cleanliness	Absence of Granulation	Flavour and/or Aroma	Total
	30	25	25	10	10	100

the ' ripeness ' and general ' goodness ' of a sample. Colour and brightness indicate the nearness to type or class: e.g. light, medium, dark etc. and afford some evidence as to whether or not the honey has been artificially ' cooked ' with a view to gaining points under the viscosity standard. ' Cooked ' honey loses its sparkle.

Cleanliness is one of the common-sense standards and takes note of the presence of any scum of air bubbles, particles of wax and any other foreign matter that may have come to the surface of the honey as a result of the normal settling process. The presence of minute crystals may also detract from the brilliance of a sample.

Clearly, honey must be of exquisite flavour but oddly enough this is one of the most difficult and unsatisfactory aspects of honey judging. The human palate is extremely sensitive and soon becomes dulled to a particular type of flavour if it is subjected to any excess of it. In practice, after tasting about five or six honey samples the normal individual finds that all honey tastes more or less the same. It is for this reason that many honey judges exhibit a fetish of continually washing the mouth with water: eating grapes: etc. etc. when occupied at the show bench. Apart from the disgusting practice of washing the mouth and spitting out the water, and the relatively expensive, although more civilised one of grape eating, it is doubtful if the desired effect is really achieved. Much more reliance can be placed on the aroma standard since the process of smelling is much more refined and although the olfactory sense may, in time, become dulled it has a much longer discriminating life than the gustatory.

Accordingly points are allocated as shown. In judging, the exhibit number is entered in the appropriate column and the merit evaluated against the relevant standard pointage. The same method applies to all classes.

Class : Granulated honey (Fig. 18)

The standards for granulated honey are: (a) general condition, i.e. freedom from frosting, dampness on the surface, evidence

FIG. 18

CLASS : GRANULATED

No.	Condition Frosting etc. 30	Quality of Granulation 20	Colour 20	Cleanliness 15	Flavour and/or Aroma 15	Total 100

of scum, freedom from fermentation, (b) quality of granulation, (c) colour, (d) cleanliness, (e) flavour and/or aroma.

Sometimes, when honey granulates, white cauliflower-like masses of crystals appear throughout the mass and when they come next to the glass wall of the jar they give the impression of

' frosting '. This detracts from the appearance of the sample. The quality, texture and hardness of the granulation involve the personal approach of the judge but it is generally accepted that the smoother and finer the granulation the more attractive the exhibit.

The colour must necessarily depend on the original colour of the liquid honey and preference is normally given to ' whiteness ' if no qualifying considerations, e.g. of classification arise.

Any minute foreign bodies show up readily in granulated honey and their presence again detracts from the value of the exhibit. The same considerations apply anent flavour and aroma as noted under liquid honey.

Some show schedules include a ' creamed ' honey class. Creamed honey is simply granulated honey of extremely soft consistency, hence the term creamed, and it is judged on the same standards as normally granulated honey.

Class : Comb honey (Fig. 19)

Comb honey on the show bench assumes various forms: e.g. sections, shallow and/or deep frames and cut comb wrapped in cellophane paper.

FIG. 19

CLASS: COMB

No.	Completeness of Filling 30	Evenness of Capping and Colour 30	Condition Freedom from Weeping and Granulation 20	Cleanliness 20	Total 100

Standards here cover (a) completeness of filling, (b) evenness of capping and colour, (c) freedom from ' weeping ' and granulation, (d) cleanliness.

The exhibited comb should be completely filled and the capping should be pure white with an even, velvet like finish. On a first class comb surface the cell outlines should be scarcely visible. Surface markings due to the tunelling of larvae of Braulae serve to handicap a sample.

Comb honey should be free from granulation. This is easily detected along the peripheral cells but its presence throughout the mass of the comb, especially if it is present in patches, can be seen more easily if a small electric torch is used to test translucency.

The wood of the frame or section should be absolutely clean and white. 'Weeping' is due to some cells of honey having absorbed, from the air, excess moisture which causes the honey to exude through the capping and spread over the surface of the comb so spoiling its appearance.

Class : Ling heather honey

The comb honey standards as given apply equally to ling heather honey when exhibited in the comb, and the granulated standards also apply when it is shown in that class.

In the liquid state the given standards and pointages for the liquid class apply but the following aspects must be noted. Ling heather honey, being of a gelatinous nature, should not ' run ' or move when the jar is inverted or tilted: it should be of a light amber colour and should contain throughout, large air bubbles. As a rule the larger the air bubble the better the sample. Many exhibitors, wrongly, heat heather honey with the object of stiffening it up. This action tends to carmelise the honey and an exception must be made in judging ling heather honey in that each sample should be tasted. Carmelisation is easily detected.

Class : Wax (Fig. 20)

Standards for wax cover (a) colour, (b) purity, (c) finish, (d) aroma.

The finest wax, rendered from cappings or virgin comb, is of a pale primrose yellow colour and good samples should approach this. There should be no evidence of foreign matter in the cake of wax exhibited and the mould should be highly polished.

Properly rendered wax has a delicate, fragrant aroma.

Fig. 20

Class : Wax

No.	Colour	Purity	Finish	Aroma	Total
	20	10	10	10	50

Class : Mead

The best mead is made from good quality honey, fermented only by yeast suitable for wine making. Nothing else should be added. This gives, on maturity, a pleasant, medium sweet product which has a certain softness to the palate. Where fermentation has been carried too far or ' wild ' yeasts have been at work, the mead will possess a certain roughness and will tend to be sour and bitter.

The sample should be clear and free from sediment of any sort.

General Points

The show schedule must be studied and judgment made in accordance with local rules.

Exhibits should be in their proper class: if not, the attention of the steward should be drawn to the mistake before any exhibit is disqualified on this basis.

Cakes of wax should be within the limits of weight stated on the schedule: if in doubt, weigh them.

Tinted grading glasses are available from bee appliance dealers. They define the upper and lower limits applicable to the shade of medium coloured honey.

Local rules with regard to presentation of exhibits, e.g. sections requiring to be wrapped in cellophane paper, glazed or not glazed, shallow or deep frames in cases, etc. must be observed in awarding prizes.

Technique No. 9

BEE DISEASE CONTROL AND DIAGNOSIS

Like all creatures honey bees are subject to certain diseases both of the adult and brood stages. Detailed information about the cause and nature of bee diseases is available in many publications perhaps the best being *The Diseases of Bees* by the late Miss A. D. Betts.[11] The reader is referred to this publication.

It is extremely difficult to prevent bees taking some or other form of disease since, if one colony becomes infected the trouble can spread quickly throughout the apiary and indeed throughout the country as happened in the case of Isle of Wight disease, owing to the fact that bees drift very readily from one colony to another. Also, bee colonies are prone to rob one another and in this way it is possible, though not as likely as is generally supposed, that disease germs may be spread. Again, it is not known precisely where any disease germ originates in the first instance and, apart from a modest standard of cleanliness in normal routine work there is little that the beekeeper can do specifically to avoid his bees contracting disease. On the other hand there *is* quite a lot that he can do to detect infection or infestation at an early stage.

It is, of course, not possible to ask questions of the bees as to their state of health and the only means at the disposal of the beekeeper is that of ' sampling '. If samples are taken regularly from colonies, that is, twice yearly, in early spring, i.e. about mid-February or early March and again about the end of August or mid-September, the presence of any infection can be detected. The health of the brood may be checked at any time during the active season and such a check of brood health should take place every time a colony is examined.

As with every other form of life, where disease is detected at an early stage, control and cure are much easier to achieve. If a disease has reached an advanced stage before it is detected the cure of the colony is virtually impossible and it is best to destroy the bees: this will avoid a weak colony being robbed out and so avoid general dissemination of the trouble.

Acarine disease

Since the source of the trouble in acarine disease is a small mite (*Acarapis woodi*) which normally lives inside the first pair of the thoracic tracheae it is clear that some form of hive fumigation which will compel the bees to breathe air containing a chemical toxic to the mite, will be most effective. Until recently such a specific substance was not available and the various fumigants tried were found to be harmful to the host as well as the parasite. A specific chemical substance, harmless to the bees but lethal to the parasitic mites has now been produced. It is called dichloro-benzoic acid and is available in an easily applied form under the trade name of ' Folbex '.

' Folbex ' takes the form of strips of absorbent paper measuring about $4 \times \frac{3}{4}$ in.: these strips are impregnated with the chemical. In addition to being impregnated with the effective chemical the strips also contain saltpeter so that when ignited, they burn slowly.

Control of acarine disease by this means is slow and altogether, a minimum of six treatments at weekly intervals is necessary. If possible, continuation of the treatment over a period of nine weeks is advantageous. Where a colony is infested with acarine disease it is wise to requeen it in addition to applying the ' Folbex ' treatment.

Since some of the bees in the colony may be temporarily overcome by the ' Folbex ' fumes this treatment can be applied only during the active season, i.e. mid-March to the end of September in most latitudes.

Method of using ' Folbex '

1. Treatment is best carried out in the evening after all the bees have returned for the day to the hive.
2. Have available a completely empty shallow super and a long nail or hat-pin.
3. Close the door of the hive by covering it with an old sack: remove the crown board and set the empty shallow box in position above the brood chamber.

4. Push the hat-pin or long nail through the 'Folbex' strip and fix the suspended strip to the inside of the shallow box distancing it about an inch or so from the side.
5. Ignite the strip with a match and see that it is smouldering properly.
6. Replace the crown board and hive roof.
7. After about ten minutes remove the roof and crown board and see that the strip has completely burned out. If it has not re-ignite it and wait until it has burned out fully before removing the shallow box.
8. Remove the shallow box and sack from the hive entrance.
9. Repeat steps 1 to 8 at least six times at weekly intervals.

If acarine disease is detected at an early stage and this simple method of treatment followed, a complete cure can be expected provided the colony has also been requeened, preferably with a young queen of known vigour.

Owing to the age immunity of the young worker bee (immunity to acarine disease is attained when the bee has reached the age of five days) timely treatment for acarine disease is usually successful but where a colony which has little or no brood is infested there is small chance of recovery since it must be remembered that it is not possible to 'cure' a diseased bee. All that can be done in treatment is to arrest the development and spread of the trouble.

When acarine disease appears in a colony during the inactive season, i.e. from October to March, it is not advisable to use 'Folbex' since a number of bees will become anaesthetised as a result of the burning saltpeter and fall away from the main winter cluster. Owing to the prevailing low temperature they will not be able to rejoin it and will accordingly die.

In this case the best chemical to use in treatment is nitrobenzene. This is applied as follows:

1. Procure a small flat tin: a cigarette, tobacco or similar tin is suitable.
2. With a nail punch about 20 to 30 holes in the bottom or lid.
3. Pack the tin with cotton wool to form an absorbent pad.
4. Charge the pad with nitrobenzene but do not over-saturate.

5. Place the tin, perforated area downwards, over the feedhole in the crown board and cover with a cloth quilt or a piece of sacking to prevent loss of fumes. If quilts are used instead of crown boards place the tin under the quilt, i.e. directly on top of the frames but, as the bees will be clustered, avoid placing it immediately above them.
6. Leave the tin in position for several weeks or until all trace of the fumes has disappeared.

After the completion of the treatment for acarine disease, by whatever method, take a sample of bees for microscopical examination and verify the success, or otherwise, of the treatment.

Nosema disease

Nosema disease is caused by a microscopic protozoon, nosema apis, which invades and destroys the epithelial cells of the midgut. Whereas acarine disease, if unchecked, will rapidly kill a colony, nosema disease is often overcome naturally by a vigorous stock. Only a poor colony, seriously reduced in numbers will die or be robbed out.

The first consideration in the treatment of nosema disease is the maintenance of vigorous stock. If ' scrub ' strains of bee are kept, nosema will always be in evidence and tend to aggravate the already low level of stock vitality.

It is doubtful, in practice, if a really satisfactory cure for nosema disease is available but the trouble may be kept in check or its effect minimised by the application of certain drugs.

The most easily obtained drug for the treatment of nosema disease is mepacrine hydrochloride. This is obtained in the form of small tablets each weighing 0·1 gm. The technique of treatment with mepacrine is simple, since the drug is merely fed to the infected colony through the medium of sugar syrup (half sugar-half water). Further, the dose to be applied is not critical. Satisfactory results have been obtained by feeding medicated sugar syrup at the level of three 0·1 gm. tablets to a 7 pound pail of syrup. At least 4 pails of feed should be given just as rapidly as the bees will take them. It is interesting to note that if any quantity of this medicated syrup is stored in the combs the resulting food is yellow in colour, like the mepacrine tablets.

Since nosema disease frequently clears up automatically, without treatment, it is difficult to assess the true value of any cure but it has been noted that where colonies have been properly treated with mepacrine there has been no recurrence of the trouble.

Another drug that may be used effectively in the treatment of nosema disease is known as ' Fumagillin '. It is available under the trade name of ' Fumidil B '. and may be obtained through wholesale chemists or from Messrs Kingsley & Keith (Chemicals) Ltd., Rex House, 38 King William Street, London, E.C.4. 'Fumidil' is available in 2 packs: the smaller contains a 0·5 gm. bottle which provides a sufficient dose for 3 colonies and the larger a 9·5 gm. bottle providing a sufficient quantity to dose 50 colonies. The 'Fumidil' is simply dissolved in 50% sugar syrup and fed to the bees in the usual manner. A satisfactory dosage is 75 mg. to the gallon of syrup but practice indicates that the amount is not critical and 100 mg. or more may be given without producing any known adverse effect on the bees. The amount of syrup fed will be governed by the strength of the infected colony and external conditions but about 1 to 1½ gallons may be given with advantage.

Bee paralysis

From time to time this peculiar trouble appears in the apiary. The exact cause of paralysis is not known but it is assumed to be of a virus nature. Where it has been definitely established that paralysis is present and that the colony is simply not being robbed (the signs are very similar) the simple technique of dusting the affected bees with flowers of sulphur forms a satisfactory treatment.

The amount of sulphur to be given is not critical but the mass of bees on each comb surface should be adequately covered with the sulphur powder. Usually two, or at most three, applications are sufficient to effect a cure. There seems to be a tendency for bee paralysis to affect certain strains of bee and it is always advisable to requeen any colony that has been treated for this disease.

Poisoning

The intense spraying programmes carried out by up to date agriculturists in the control of weeds, etc. creates difficulties for the beekeeper in that quite an amount of spray drifts into ditches and similar places where bees obtain their drinking water. Poisonous substances can therefore easily be carried back to the hive with the result that many adult bees become poisoned as the water is distributed throughout the hive population and a very high death rate can result. It is possible of course to close bees in for a short time when poisonous spraying is to be carried out in the vicinity of an apiary but this is not a satisfactory solution since the effect of the spraying may well last for several days.

Where poisoning occurs the best antidote is the feeding of dilute sugar syrup. The dilute syrup provides the bees with all the water they would normally collect out of doors and at the same time acts as a most useful stimulant and serves to restore the morale of the colony.

European Foul Brood

The cause of this disorder is not definitely known in spite of many scientific efforts to establish a particular bacterium as the causative agent. In fact, European Foul Brood does not appear to be caused by any *specific* germ. Practical experience gained in working with this disorder suggests that the real cause of larval death is constitutional weakness. This weakness may be inherent in the larvae or it may be associated with some deficiency in the larval food as elaborated by the nurse bees. It has also been suggested that soil peculiarity or deficiency, affecting nectar secretion and thus the honey flow, could be reflected in the appearance of European Foul Brood and there may well be some connection if the strain of bee used in such a locality is not vigorous.

Practice has shown, however, that the remedy for this disorder is simply the requeening of the colony with a queen of an entirely different strain. No interval between dequeening and requeening is necessary or desirable. Contrary to what is generally asserted my experience with this condition shows that the trouble is *not* infectious and combs of dead and dying E.F.B. infected larvae may be inserted into any strong and vigorous colony without any trace of trouble resulting.

Antibiotics may also be used with the object of clearing up an E.F.B. condition. American work suggests that Terramycin is the most efficient drug. The dosage is 25 mg. active terramycin, i.e. about one teaspoonful, per colony, fed to the bees in sugar syrup (50%). Five to 6 weekly doses are necessary to allow the colony to regain its morale. Alternatively the terramycin may be mixed with icing sugar in a 50/50 proportion and applied to the colony as a dust. The same dosage of terramycin is given and treatment should cover a 5 to 6 week period. The effect of this antibiotic is simply to keep in check the lethal factors which bring about the death of the larvae; in other words, the antibiotic increases the *vitality* of the larvae. This state of affairs, however, does not last and if the affected colony is not requeened with a vigorous queen, feeding with medicated syrup must be resorted to at frequent intervals if the larvae are to show some semblance of health and the adult population of the colony is to be maintained. Even so, the adult bees reared under such conditions prove themselves to be unstable and weak constitutionally so that an already poor stock condition is really aggravated.

American Foul Brood

In marked contrast to European Foul Brood, American Foul Brood disease of the honey bee larvae can be shown to be due to infection with a specific bacillus (*Bacillus larvae*).

Since the cause is known it is possible to select a specific drug to use against this disease. While any of the sulphonamide series of drugs may be used, the most useful is sulphathiazole. Sulphathiazole is easily obtained from any chemist either in tablet or powder form. It may be applied by feeding, in medicated sugar syrup (50%), or in powder form, by dusting directly on to the combs and bees in the affected colony. The dosage is not critical but when using a drug of this nature *heavy* initial dosage is *essential*. If this is not done and an initial ' knock out ' dose is not given the possibility exists that *all* the bacteria will not be immobilised and some may indeed become tolerant to the drug.

If sulphathiazole is fed in sugar syrup it should be given at the rate of 1 gm. (i.e. 2 tablets) per 7 pound pail of feed. Feeding should be at the rate of one pail per week over a period of 6 weeks, or until such time as all trace of disease has disappeared. If the colony is reasonably strong it will be found that a 4 feed course of treatment is normally adequate. It is not *necessary* to remove from the brood chamber any of the infected combs but the opportunity should be taken to renew any old or badly built combs. It is also advisable to uncap, by bruising, all sealed honey in the brood chamber.

The dusting technique is neater and more efficient than that of feeding the sulphathiazole. The pulverised sulphathiazole is dusted on to the combs and bees in the infected stock by means of a powder distributor.

Any powder distributor, such as is used in the application of insecticidal horticultural dusts is satisfactory. The comb surfaces as well as the bees covering them should be liberally covered with the powder. There is no danger of giving an overdose. Dustings are best given at weekly intervals over a period of 4 to 6 weeks. Disinfection of any equipment associated with the treated colony is not necessary. American Foul Brood is not nearly so infectious as is supposed and a mass inoculation of healthy larvae is necessary for the disease to appear. Sulphathiazole effects a permanent cure in the case of American Foul Brood and no recurrence of the disease will occur if the above technique is carried out. This does not mean to say however that a colony will never be reinfected. If this were assumed it would be tantamount to suggesting that sulphathiazole bestows permanent immunity to the disease.

As far as is known no type of bee is immune to American Foul Brood but some strains are better than others in removing affected larvae from the combs and thus keeping the disease in check. The impression may, therefore, be given of mild immunity.

It should be noted that American Foul Brood takes quite a long time to kill a colony of bees. My experience shows that it is only after three years of infection that a weakened colony is unable to clear away the dead and putrefying larvae. As a result it presents the typical A.F.B. state.

Chilled brood

Chilled brood can arise through the premature spreading of brood combs in the brood chamber especially in early spring. When brood dies as a result of chilling it turns black as distinct from the brown colouration shown when larvae die from brood disease. Any colony of bees which has lost brood through chilling tends to be low in morale and the best way to restore this is to give the bees a feeder of warm, dilute, sugar syrup. Several feeds may be required before a satisfactory brood nest is re-established.

Sack brood

This is another peculiar disorder of the brood of the honey bee. The cause has not yet been positively established but it is said to be a filtrable virus. This trouble is not common but where it does arise the best plan is to requeen the colony and, if the population of the hive has declined appreciably, the situation may be restored quite rapidly by giving several feeds of sugar syrup.

Chalk brood

Chalk brood, caused by a fungus (*Pericystus apis*) is sporadic in its appearance and frequently the bees are able to clean it up on their own, once the colony reaches full development at mid-summer. A high incidence of infected larvae in any colony usually indicates some constitutional weakness in the strain and it is wise to requeen a badly infected stock.

Very badly infected combs can be removed but as a rule the bees are able to clear out the chalky larvae on their own and unless combs are in bad condition and warrant renewal there is no point in destroying them.

Diagnosis of acarine disease

Field. Early diagnosis of acarine disease is not possible by any ' on the spot ' field test. As a rule the trouble has reached an advanced stage before there are any clinical signs that disease is present.

Affected bees are unable to fly and they crawl from the hive in large numbers. Small groups congregate together around the stems of grass and many of the bees appear to have the wings slightly dislocated so that they assume the form of the letter ' K '. In addition there may be quite an amount of staining of the hive as a result of excrement being voided immediately inside and around the hive entrance. When bees are not able to void their faeces on the wing there is usually a great deal of soiling in and around the hive. Many bees also have the abdomen unduly swollen owing to the retention of large amounts of faecal matter. However, the presence of retained excreta in the colon does not necessarily mean that the bee is suffering from acarine disease. The foraging population of a colony may be decimated almost overnight in severe attacks.

F

Laboratory. In order to diagnose accurately the presence of mite infestation of a honey bee a simple dissection must be made so that the seat of the infestation, i.e. the first thoracic tracheae, can be examined. The dissection is easy to perform and may be made under any low powered, simple microscope although it is much more satisfactory to use a proper binocular dissecting instrument.

Apparatus required

> Scalpel or sharp penknife.
> Entomological forceps.
> Two dissecting needles.
> Small platform of wood or cork on which to work with the specimen.
> Dissecting microscope. This may be a very simple lens or an elaborate binocular type microscope.

It is best to work with reasonably fresh material: bees that have been dead from 24 to 48 hours are most easily dealt with. If a live sample is to hand it is best to kill the bees by inserting the sample box (open) into a killing jar, or to introduce a small piece of blotting paper soaked in amyl acetate into the match box and wait until the bees are dead or almost so. An ordinary one pound honey jar makes a useful killing bottle. The bottom of the jar should be covered with several thicknesses of blotting paper so that a firm pad about $\frac{1}{4}$ inch thick is formed. This pad is soaked (not drenched) with amyl acetate and the jar lid screwed firmly on. For use the match box of bees is partially opened and quickly placed in the killing jar.

After a minute or so the bees will be dead, or at any rate completely immobilised so that they can be dissected easily. Amyl acetate has the advantage that the killed insect remains completely relaxed.

Method

1. Take up a bee with the forceps and place it on its back on the dissecting platform.
2. With a dissecting needle impale the bee through the thorax and insert the blade of the scalpel or penknife behind the first

pair of legs. Push gently downwards and forwards so pushing away the head and first pair of legs.

3. The thorax cavity will now be exposed and the impaled bee is transferred under the microscope.

4. The major portion of the tracheae can now be seen and by careful manipulation with a second dissecting needle the whole of each trachea can be examined.

If the bee is free from mite infestation the tracheae will be milky white in appearance. Any darkening of colour or browning of the tracheae indicates the presence of acarine mites. The degree of infestation of the individual can be estimated by the extent of the staining. It is not, of course, possible to see individual mites by means of the simple dissecting microscope: their presence only may be detected. In order to see individual mites a compound microscope must be used and the tracheae must be dissected out from the thorax and transferred to a microscope slide.

Detailed examination can be made when the specimen is mounted under a cover glass. If the muscular tissue in the thorax is at all fresh it will often be difficult to dissect the tracheae away cleanly. It is an advantage here to cut away that part of the thorax containing the first thoracic spiracles and immerse it for a few minutes in some 10% caustic soda solution. This may be done conveniently in a watch glass. The caustic soda solution will free the muscle tissue which can then be removed easily, leaving the tracheae more or less freely outlined against the dark brown chitin of the thorax. The tracheae can now be transferred easily by means of a needle to the micro slide, a drop of glycerine jelly or similar mountant applied and a cover glass laid on. The detailed structure of the mites may now be studied at different magnifications. Apart from size the male and female mites are easy to distinguish. The females have two long hairs attached to the last pair of legs while the males have only one such long hair.

Diagnosis of nosema disease

Field. Nosema disease is difficult to diagnose by any ' field ' test. There may be signs of distress in an infected colony and a certain degree of soiling of the hive interior and entrance. An infected colony rapidly becomes depopulated. This occurrence has been given various names including ' Spring Dwindling ', ' Disappearing Disease ', etc. Nosema infection can only be diagnosed with certainty in the laboratory.

Laboratory. Since evidence of the presence of nosema disease. will be found in the gut of the bee it is necessary to remove the digestive system for examination. This presents no difficulty if the bee is either alive or taken fresh from the killing jar. Hold the bee firmly between the finger and thumb of the left hand (or pin it down by means of a dissecting needle to a piece of cork board) and grip the tail end firmly with forceps. A gentle pull should bring out the colon, small intestine and stomach, complete. If the bee is fresh only a little practice will make this operation very easy. Lay the intestines on a glass slide, add a very small drop of water and a drop of nigrosin stain. Now lay on a cover glass and press gently so that the mass of gut is evenly squashed. The preparation should be examined under the microscope at a magnification of $\times 400$. If nosema spores are present they will show up as tiny clear oval bodies against the black background produced by the nigrosin stain.

If a permanent preparation is desired lay the gut on the micro slide, add a drop of water and a drop of nigrosin stain and macerate the material with a glass rod. With the forceps remove the larger pieces of gut and smooth out the remains so that a smear is left. Now dry the slide carefully on a hot plate. If this is not available a convenient, if unorthodox way is to place the slide on top of the microscope lamp where it will dry quite nicely. When dry add a drop of ' Euparal Vert ' mountant and apply a cover glass. Label the slide.

A quick way of determining the presence of nosema in a sample of bees, i.e. 20 or so, is to chop off the abdomens and crush them in a small mortar, adding a few drops of water. A smear of the sediment can be made, as outlined above, and the presence of nosema spores determined. It should be appreciated that only the spores of nosema will show up clearly by the nigrosin smear technique. If the other stages in the development of nosema are to be studied a staining technique must be used. A satisfactory stain is Heidenhain's Iron Haematoxylin. Two solutions are required : Heidenhain's soln. A, iron alum, and Heidenhain's B, haematoxylin soln.

Method

1. Immerse the slide containing the smear (or gut section: see micro technique) in soln. ' A ' for 12 to 24 hours.

2. Rinse in water.

3. Transfer to soln. ' B ' for about the same time as was given to soln. ' A '.

4. Rinse in water.

5. Transfer to soln. ' A ' to differentiate. (see note). The correct degree of differentiation is determined by examination under the microscope.

6. Wash in running water for about 5 minutes.

7. Counter stain, if required (see micro technique).

8. If sectioned material is being handled, dehydrate, clear and mount (see micro technique). If the preparation is a smear it will be sufficient to dry carefully and mount in ' Euparal Vert '.

Note: Differentiation. After staining as at stage 3 above no detail will be visible in the preparation. De-staining, or differentiation will take place on re-immersing the preparation in soln. ' A ' and, when the correct amount of detail has become visible, as determined by successive examinations under the microscope, the differentiation process is stopped by washing the slide in water.

Diagnosis of amoeba disease

Field. As in the case of nosema disease this disorder is difficult, if not impossible, to diagnose in the field. Infected colonies usually show signs of dwindling but the precise cause of loss of bees can only be determined by laboratory examination of suspected material.

Laboratory. It is not easy to diagnose amoeba infection by means of the smear technique. The gut from suspected bees should be prepared for sectioning (see micro technique) and stained in Heidenhain's haematoxylin as in the nosema diagnosis technique. If present the amoeba cysts will show up clearly in the Malpighian tubes.

Diagnosis of bee paralysis

Field. Individual bees affected with this disorder appear to be recognised by the healthy members of the colony who take immediate steps to expel them from the hive. The diseased bees are subjected to considerable rough handling as they are dragged from the hive. Many attempt to re-enter after their expulsion and this continual rough handling soon deprives the infected bee of most of the body hairs. The result is that the bee assumes a black and shiny, polished appearance. This pattern of behaviour must not be confused with that of robbing but experience will soon indicate whether or not robbing bees are around. If the behaviour of the bee is furtive and determined then it is a robber.

There may also be a distinctive smell about the infected bee. Odours are difficult to define but on occasions it is possible to detect something of a ' fishy ' smell about paralysis infected bees.

Laboratory. Gut material which should include the region where the malpighian tubes enter the small intestine is prepared, sectioned and stained with safranin and methyl violet. Paralysis infection is determined by the presence of what are called ' inclusion bodies ' (because they are included within the cell boundaries) which are stained bright red by the safranin and are easily distinguished from the surrounding tissue which is stained variously from violet to red. The ' inclusion bodies ' which vary in number and size are found in the epithelial cells of the anterior end of the small intestine. In advanced cases of paralysis they appear in large numbers and are easily seen. Otherwise they may be difficult to spot. They are either spherical or ellipsoidal in form and measure from 1 to 8 microns in diameter.

Method

It is assumed that the appropriate material has been prepared and sectioned (see micro technique) and that the wax embedded sections are properly fixed to the micro slides.

1. Warm the slides gently, until there is the faintest sign that the wax is about to melt. This operation must be done with great care otherwise the wax will melt too rapidly and the fragile section of tissue may be destroyed.
2. Transfer to xylol. 2 mins.

3. Transfer to xylol : alcohol (50:50) 2 mins.
4. Transfer to alcohol (95%) 2 mins.
5. Transfer to alcohol (75%) 2 mins.
6. Transfer to safranin (alcoholic stain) 5 : 10 mins.
7. Wash in alcohol (70%) 1 min.
8. Transfer to methyl violet (alcoholic stain) 5 : 10 mins.
9. Wash in alcohol (70%) 1 min.
10. Transfer to alcohol (75%) 2 mins.
11. Transfer to alcohol (90%) 2 mins.
12. Transfer to alcohol (95%) 2 mins.
13. Clear in clove oil, 10 mins. or longer. This is done by covering the sections with a large smear of clove oil.
14. Wash off the clove oil with xylol. Do this rapidly to remove all the clove oil.
15. Mount in ' Euparal Vert ' or Canada balsam.
16. Label.

Diagnosis of poisoning

Field. The certain diagnosis of poisoning is not easy. However, if there is a sudden and catastrophic death rate in any colony some form of spray poisoning must be suspected. The many forms of poisonous spray in use today act variously on the honey bee but usually the first indication of trouble is the rapid decrease in field population. Frequently, although not always, there is a marked death rate of bees around the hive entrance.

In severe cases young ' hive ' bees are also killed in large numbers and this leads to the neglect of brood rearing with the consequent chilling of brood and the rapid death of the colony. Many of the adult bees die with the tongue extended.

Laboratory. In view of the complex nature of the poisons used by spraying contractors, accurate diagnosis of the harmful agent is outwith the scope of the ' bee laboratory '. A sample of the dead and/or dying bees should be sent as quickly as possible to the nearest county analyst who is best qualified to determine the exact nature of the poison.

Diagnosis of European Foul Brood

Field. In almost every case it is the *unsealed* brood that is affected although occasionally a certain amount of brood may be sealed before death occurs. Most strains of bee make some attempt to remove the dead larvae and it has for long been recognised that the ' yellow ', i.e. Italian type, is always active in this respect.

The larvae assume unnatural positions in the cells and gradually change colour from white to yellow then to dark brown. The decaying larvae usually have a pronounced acrid odour but it is difficult to give a precise definition. The larval remains may in some cases be of a ropy consistency but usually no ' ropiness ' is apparent: the remains dry up into a smooth scale which is easily removed from the cell.

Laboratory. Several forms of bacteria are present in larvae which show typical signs of European Foul Brood and their *certain* identification is difficult. This is particularly so when it is noted that the causative agent, *Streptococcus pluton*, may occur in several forms. It is, however, possible to make a fairly accurate diagnosis by making a nigrosin smear of larval remains and examining the preparation under a high power of the microscope using the 4 mm. oil immersion objective and a $\times 5$ or $\times 10$ eyepiece. After some practice, rods and spores (which show up clearly against a black background) of *Bacillus alvei* will be picked out as well as the pointed oval form of *Streptococcus pluton*. *Streptococcus pluton* is an extremely small organism being about 1 micron in length. It must be realised that it is not at all easy to be *certain* of the particular type of organisms seen under the microscope and it is advisable to have one's findings checked by a specialist in the field of bee diseases until some experience has been gained in microscopy.

Method

Transfer a portion of larval remains to a micro slide, add a drop of water and a drop of nigrosin stain. Mix thoroughly and smear out to make a thin film. Dry, apply a drop of mountant and finish the preparation with a cover glass.

Note. The micron, usually designated by the Greek letter μ (pronounced *mew*) is the microscopists unit of measurement. It is equivalent to 1/1000 of a millimetre or 1/25,000 of an inch.

Diagnosis of American Foul Brood

Field. American Foul Brood is perhaps the easiest of the brood diseases to diagnose. Only the sealed brood is attacked and the larvae usually die at the pre-pupal stage. The cell cappings are usually sunken, i.e. concave and many show signs of having been pierced. This piercing of the cappings is due to the workers making an attempt to clear up the decaying larvae. It would seem that after some initial clearing the bees lose their morale and after piercing the capping they give up this activity. As the larvae decay a characteristic smell is given off. Again it is not wise to define precisely the nature of this odour but it is slightly reminiscent of rotting glue. The larvae change colour from white to yellow then to a brown, coffee colour and finally to a very dark brown. At the height of decay the moist larval remains assume an elastic-like consistency and may be drawn out like an elastic band. When the larval remains finally dry they harden into a scale which cannot be removed from the cell since it sticks firmly to the lower angle.

Laboratory. The easiest way to make a laboratory test for American Foul Brood is to prepare a nigrosin smear as described in the case of European Foul Brood. The decaying material or comb fragment containing some scale material is moistened with a drop of water and a drop of nigrosin stain applied. The smear is then dried and finally mounted in ' Euparal Vert '. The spores of *Bacillus* larvae are again very small measuring about 1·3 microns long and they show up as clear white objects against the black background.

Another useful test for American Foul Brood is the Milk Test. This is a simple and effective technique and depends on the fact that the A.F.B. bacillus has certain properties that are able to ' clear ' a milky solution. Fresh milk, skim milk or milk powder may be used but the milky solution should be made up immediately before use so that it is in a fresh condition. This test works most satisfactorily if warm water is used.

Method

1. Place the A.F.B. material, i.e. either a scale or ropy larval remains, into a test tube and add about 20 drops of warm

water. Shake gently to incorporate the material into a watery solution.

2. Dilute a small quantity of milk with water or reconstitute a little of the milk powder and add about 10 drops of this to the test tube containing the A.F.B. material. Again shake the tube gently.

3. Keep the test tube warm.

Within 15 minutes the milky, cloudy solution will have cleared if American Foul Brood is present.

In carrying out a test of this nature it is always wise to run a control: i.e. a similar test but with the suspected material omitted. At the end of 15 minutes a comparison of the clarity of the two liquids will give a clear indication as to the presence of American Foul Brood.

Diagnosis of sack brood

Field. This disorder affects the sealed brood. The larvae are usually of a dull white to off white colour although they may change to yellow or brown. There is normally no particular odour but when putrefaction sets in some degree of stench may be perceived. The skin of the dead larvae becomes very tough and it is possible to pull a larva out of its cell without breaking the skin. As a result of this characteristic the dead grub when pulled out resembles a sack: hence the name sack brood. The contents of this larval sack are watery and appear granular in nature. When the larva finally dries up it forms a scale which is easily removed from the cell.

Laboratory. If a nigrosin smear is made of the larval remains it is usually found to be sterile, no bacterial forms being visible.

Diagnosis of chalk brood

Field. Only sealed brood is affected. The dead larvae are most frequently ' off white ' in colour but sometimes they may turn a slaty grey or green. Occasionally they may appear almost black. The dead larvae harden into chalk-like mummies which are easily removed from the combs. There is no particular smell associated with chalk brood.

Laboratory. Place a small portion of chalky larval remains on a micro slide, add a drop of water and a cover glass and examine under a low power of the microscope. The white hyphae of the fungus will be clearly seen. These are commonly likened to cotton wool fibres. Cysts containing spores of the fungus may also be seen. These spores are roughly oval in shape and measure approximately 3 microns by 2 microns.

Diagnosis of addled brood

Field. This condition is usually associated with sealed brood but it may be found in brood at all stages of development from eggs and newly hatched larvae to bees fully formed and just about to emerge. The dead brood is normally of a grey colour but may have a blotchy appearance. As a rule there is no special odour but if putrefaction has occurred there may be a sour and slightly offensive odour. There is usually no scale formed.

Laboratory. Since the larval or pupal remains appear to be sterile no bacterial forms appear when a nigrosin smear is examined under the microscope.

Diagnosis of chilled brood

Field. All stages of brood development are liable to suffer from chilling. The dead brood loses its scintillating white colour and turns black. Usually there is no odour but again if there should be any degree of putrefaction a sourish offensive smell will be noted. Chilling usually results in the brood dying uniformly.

How to take a sample of bees

Various devices have been suggested to facilitate the taking of a sample of bees for microscopical examination but the simplest way is to pick the bees either from the feed hole in the crown board or quilt or directly from the comb surface. Bees are best picked up by the wings: in this way they are unable to sting.

The handiest and most useful container for a bee sample is a match box. Have available for every match box a piece of gummed paper measuring about $\frac{3}{4}$ inch square. Punch a hole in one side of the match box about $\frac{3}{8}$ inch in diameter; this size is easily covered by a finger and is large enough to pop a bee through.

As each bee is picked up it is placed in the match box and the hole conveniently covered by a finger until the required number of bees has been taken. The gummed piece of paper is then

TABLE 4

Percentage of infested bees in colony	Number of bees that must be examined in order to give an 80%, 95% and 99% chance of finding at least one diseased bee in the sample		
	80%	95%	99%
95	1	1	2
90	1	2	2
85	1	2	3
80	1	2	3
75	2	3	4
70	2	3	4
65	2	3	5
60	2	4	5
55	2	4	6
50	3	5	7
45	3	5	8
40	3	6	9
35	4	7	11
30	5	8	13
25	6	10	16
20	7	13	21
15	10	18	28
10	15	28	44
5	31	58	89
1	161	298	457

licked on the back and slid over the hole thus effectively closing it. For the detection of disease a sample should number about 20 to 30 bees (Table 4). Mark the match box clearly with its identification number so that subsequent confusion is avoided.

Technique No. 10

MICROSCOPY

The subject of microscopy is complex and difficult and no attempt will be made here other than to deal with those techniques which are relevant to the study of the honey bee. There are many excellent detailed books on microscopy but perhaps the best for elementary work is that of Peacock.[12]

While a certain amount of work on the bee may be done with only modest apparatus it must be appreciated that for technique, involving wax embedding and sectioning of bee gut for example, makeshift apparatus is entirely out of the question. However, the keen student may well have access to a laboratory where his material may be prepared, sectioned, stained and mounted.

All that will be required then is a reasonably good microscope so that the prepared slides can be studied at leisure.

Essential apparatus

Microscopes

Two microscopes. (*a*) dissecting
(*b*) compound.

The dissecting microscope may be of extremely simple design and excellent work may be done with a good watchmaker's eye-glass, suitably mounted, or any other lens which allows a reasonable working distance. The ideal is, of course, a binocular instrument which greatly facilitates and speeds up work where a number of bee samples have to be examined, e.g. for acarine disease infestation.

The compound microscope should be capable of giving magnifications up to × 1000.

Compound microscopes are expensive instruments but good second hand models are usually fairly easily obtainable. If you have little or no experience of microscopes it is advisable to get the opinion of an experienced microscopist before purchasing an instrument, either new or second hand.

Wax embedding oven

For satisfactory wax impregnation of tissue this piece of apparatus is desirable. It is, of course, expensive but in this instance it is possible to improvise and quite a satisfactory oven can be constructed from a suitably sized biscuit tin heated by means of small electric light bulbs. The purpose of the embedding oven is to maintain the wax in which the tissue is being embedded at a temperature just above that of the melting point of the wax used.

It is usual to use wax having a melting point of $53°$ C. Some form of thermostatic control will be necessary in order to avoid overheating and spoiling of the tissue during the process of preparation.

Microtome

The usual small laboratory instrument is known as the Cambridge Rocking Microtome. This again is an expensive item of equipment but it is essential for satisfactory sectioning. While sections of plant and some animal tissue may be made using a simple hand microtome it is impossible to use the hand instrument for bee work. The use of the microtome is fully described in the relevant literature.

Brass ' L ' pieces or Paper Trays

These are required to hold the wax in which the tissue is being embedded. Suitable ' L ' pieces may be made from material having a thickness of 12 mm. The arms of the ' L ' should measure approximately 25 mm. by 60 mm. thus allowing for some variation in the size of wax block cast. Small paper trays measuring 10 mm. $\times$ 10 mm. $\times$ 25 mm. are easily made and form a useful size for normal bee work.

Staining jars

A number of these will be required. Specially made jars are available but some improvisation is permissible here so long as the jars will accommodate at least two micro slides, and are not too large. The larger the jar the more stain, etc. that will be required.

Dissecting needles and forceps

Standard patterns easily obtained from laboratory furnishers are suitable.

Paraffin wax

This is required for embedding the tissue and should have a melting point of 53° C.

Micro slides and cover glasses

The slides should be the standard 3×1 in. size and the cover glasses $2 \times \frac{7}{8}$ in. No. 2, and $\frac{7}{8} \times \frac{7}{8}$ in. No. 2. Cover glasses can be obtained round as well as square and they are made in several thicknesses: No. 0 from ·07-·13 mm., No. 1 from ·13-·17 mm., No. 2 from ·17-·21 mm. and No. 3 from ·21-·35 mm.

Watch glasses

One or two watch glasses of varying size will be required.

Sundry items

Glassware such as flasks, beakers small specimen jars, wash bottle (although this is usually made of plastic nowadays) and the homely pie-dish are essentials on the bench.

Preparation of material for microscopic examination

General outline

If the detailed structure of delicate tissue, such as any part of the gut of the bee, is to be studied, cross and longitudinal sections of the selected material must be prepared. For this a special technique is necessary so that the soft tissue may be satisfactorily cut into very thin sections. These sections must not be more than 12 microns thick, otherwise the detail will not be visible, and it is usual to cut them to a thickness of about 8 microns.

Fresh material from the bee, unless specially treated, will deteriorate rapidly so that it must be preserved in a state as near as possible to that of the ' live ' condition. This means that the tissue must be ' killed ' and ' fixed ' in the ' near live ' state and at the same time satisfactorily preserved. This is in fact achieved by a process known as ' fixation '.

A number of ' fixatives ' are available but the most useful for our purpose is Bouin's Picro Formol. This may be made up in the laboratory but it is readily obtainable from suppliers of laboratory chemicals.

After ' fixation ' the material is washed in alcohol to remove the surplus fixative, then it is preserved until required in alcohol. Absolute alcohol is expensive and for routine purposes not essential. Satisfactory work can be done using 95% spirit which is easily obtained and a licence is not required.

In order to support the tissue while it is being cut into thin sections some form of embedding medium is necessary and paraffin wax is eminently suitable for this purpose.

Since the tissue has been preserved in alcohol, which is not miscible with wax, the alcohol must be removed in favour of a liquid which *is* miscible with paraffin wax. This is accomplished by transferring the material to a vessel containing equal parts alcohol and cedar wood oil. The alcohol does not, of course, mix with the oil so that a discontinuous layer is formed at the junction of the two liquids. The material when transferred to this medium will, at first, come to rest at the bottom of the alcohol layer then gradually, as the alcohol is expelled, it will sink to the bottom of the oil layer.

At this stage the material is transferred to a container of pure cedar oil where the final expulsion of alcohol takes place.

Next, wax baths are prepared. Small crucibles form useful containers. Bath No. 1 contains 75% cedar oil and 25% wax: Bath No. 2, 50% cedar oil and 50% wax: Bath No. 3, 75% wax and 25% cedar oil and Bath No. 4, 100% wax. The material is moved successively through the various baths and, having reached the final bath, it is ready for embedding and subsequent sectioning.

Sectioning is a delicate operation and must be carried out by means of a specially designed instrument called a microtome.

After sectioning on the microtome the thin 'slices' must be firmly fixed to the micro slides. Next, the wax must be removed. This is done by immersing the slide in xylol, a powerful wax solvent.

If the sections are examined under the microscope at this stage very little detailed structure, if any, will be seen. The tissue must now be stained so that the structure, and any abnormality due to disease, etc. may be made visible. Since stains are usually dissolved either in water or alcohol the slide containing the sections must be suitably conditioned to the degree of water or alcohol present in the stain. Consequently the xylol is removed by immersing the slide in 95% alcohol and subsequently moving it through descending grades of alcohol until it reaches the grade corresponding to that of the stain. If the stain is contained in 70% alcohol then the sections can go straight from the 70% alcohol to the staining jar.

On the other hand if the stain is an aqueous one it will be necessary to take the sections right down to the 30% grade alcohol before transferring them to the staining jar.

Once the sections are stained they must retrace their steps through the various ascending grades of alcohol until finally they reach the 95% level.

Before a permanent mount can be made this alcohol must be removed and the tissue cleared so that a final mounting medium may be applied. Mounting media are usually of a resinous nature and will not mix with alcohol. The alcohol is removed by placing the sections first of all in a xylol/alcohol (50:50) mixture then in pure xylol.

Finally a drop of mountant is applied (this is usually Canada balsam or Euparal) and a cover glass carefully laid on. The permanent mount is finally labelled.

The Mid Gut: Detailed technique

Where it is desired to study, microscopically, the structure of the mid gut of the bee the following method of wax embedding and staining with haematoxylin and eosin will be found satisfactory. The haematoxylin stains the nuclei blue: the cytoplasm and muscle are stained pink.

G

Method

1. Take a freshly killed bee or, preferably one that is still alive and with the fine forceps grasp the tip of the abdomen and gently, but steadily pull out the alimentary tract.

2. Drop the gut into Bouin's picro formol. (It will be advisable to remove the gut from several bees so that plenty of material will be available.) The material should remain in the fixative from 12 to 24 hours.

3. Remove from the Bouin solution and wash the material in alcohol. This may conveniently be done in a watch glass.

4. Transfer to 95% alcohol until required or, if the work is to proceed immediately, to a small wide-mouthed jar containing half cedar oil and half alcohol.

5. The gut will come to rest at the junction of the two liquids and, after some time (usually a day or two) it will gradually sink down into the cedar oil.

6. Transfer to a bath of pure cedar oil and leave until the gut has a clear, translucent appearance. This stage is reached when all the alcohol has been removed from the tissues.

7. Transfer to embedding bath No. 1 which has been placed in the embedding oven (or substitute device) and contains the just molten wax. The four embedding baths must, of course, be placed in the oven which is adjusted to maintain a temperature of about 55° C. so that the wax is kept at a temperature just above its melting point.

8. Allow the tissue to remain for several hours in each of the embedding baths in turn and once it has reached the bath of pure wax allow it to remain there for at least 12 hours in order to ensure that the wax has permeated the tissue thoroughly.

9. Melt a small quantity of the embedding wax in a suitable tin or dish and arrange the brass ' L ' pieces on a small plate of *warmed* glass, so that they form a rectangle measuring 25 × 15 cm. The ' L ' pieces conveniently form a mould into which the tissue can be placed.

10. Pour the molten wax into the mould until it is just over half full.

11. With warmed forceps transfer the gut from the pure wax bath in the embedding oven to the mould and roughly orient it,

using warmed needles. Forceps, etc. are conveniently warmed in the flame of a Bunsen burner or spirit lamp.

12. Add a little more molten wax and finally, with warmed dissecting needles, orient the material so that it is positioned about the mid point of the mould. The final orientation will depend upon whether transverse or longitudinal sections are to be cut.

13. Add sufficient molten wax to fill the mould and when a skin has formed on the top of the wax, plunge the mould into a dish of cold water so that all the wax cools rapidly. The outline of the gut will be easily seen through the wax, which facilitates the trimming of the block according to which part of the gut it is desired to section. In our case we wish to section the mid gut so that quite a bit of the wax block can be trimmed away.

14. The trimming of the wax block looks a simple operation but it can occasion quite a bit of trouble. Use a really sharp knife and as far as possible cut all surfaces at right angles to one another.

15. Fix the wax block to the microtome chuck. This is best done by coating the end of the chuck with molten wax. This cools and forms a foundation. Melt the surface of this foundation with the heated blade of a scalpel or penknife and press the wax block firmly on to the base so that the edges will be parallel with the edge of the microtome razor.

16. Adjust the microtome to cut sections of about 8 microns thickness. Fix the razor, which must be clean and sharp, so that the end of the wax block just clears it when the arm of the microtome is raised and lowered.

17. Commence cutting. If the surfaces of the wax block have been cut squarely a wax ribbon of sections will come off the edge of the razor at right angles to it. If the surfaces are *not* square the sections will come off circular wise, which is not so convenient.

18. The sections composing the ribbon will be wrinkled to a greater or lesser degree so that before fixing them to a slide they must be smoothed out. This is most easily done by carefully taking a portion of the wax ribbon and floating it on top of some warm (not hot) water. The pie-dish forms

a convenient water bath for this operation. The heat of the water will expand the sections so that they are easily transferred to a slide. While a single section can be allocated to a slide it is usual to fix several but sufficient room must be left on the slide for the label.

19. Since the sectioned tissue is to be subjected to immersion in a variety of liquids it must be fixed firmly to the glass slide. To do this take a clean slide and, very sparingly, rub over the surface with a fluid called Mayers albumen. (This again is easily obtained from the laboratory chemical supplier.) If you don't have any of this handy, ordinary saliva is an adequate and cheap substitute. Apply some spittle, genteely, to the slide and make an even but thin smear over the surface.

20. Pass the slide carefully under the expanded ribbon of sections which is floating on the surface of the water and raise it up gently so that the required number of sections is taken. Orient the sections on the slide.

21. Drain off the surplus water and stand the glass slides on end to dry. A warm atmosphere will help here but do not try to speed up this operation too much otherwise the wax will melt and the sections become distorted. It is important that the slides are quite dry before proceeding further. Failure to observe this direction will result in the tissue coming away from the slide in the subsequent processes of staining, dehydration, etc.

22. When completely dry transfer the slides (two may be taken at a time and handled back to back) to pure xylol in order to dissolve the wax. It is permissible to warm the slide gently until there is just a suggestion that the wax is beginning to melt but it is best to avoid this, if possible.
    Allow about 2 mins. in this bath.

23. Transfer to xylol/alcohol (half and half) 2 mins.

24. Transfer to 95% alcohol 2 mins.

25. Transfer to 90% alcohol 2 mins. (see table 5).

26. Transfer to 70% alcohol 2 mins.

27. Transfer to 50% alcohol 2 mins.

28. Transfer to 30% alcohol 2 mins.

29. Stain in Delafields haematoxylin approx. 5 mins. The stain should be diluted with about 3 parts water to 1 part

stain. At this stage the process and degree of staining should be observed from time to time under the microscope. When the tissue seems fairly well stained, differentiate in acid alcohol for a moment or two.

30. Wash in tap water. This has the effect of 'bluing' the haematoxylin.

31. Transfer to the eosin stain, about 1 min.

32. Dehydrate through ascending grades of alcohol: i.e. 70%, 90%, 95%, quickly, allowing a moment or two in each grade. If this process is prolonged the eosin will be washed out.

33. Transfer to alcohol/xylol then quickly to xylol. The sections may remain for some time in the pure xylol if necessary.

34. Remove from the xylol: apply a drop of 'Euparal Vert' and complete the mount with a suitable cover glass.

35. Label.

Preparation of wings, sting, legs, etc.

Useful micro slides of the hard or chitinous parts of the bee as well as the sting are fairly easy to prepare and form useful preliminary exercises. While there are several refined and more elaborate methods of making preparations of, e.g. wings, legs, antennae, etc., the following simple techniques have proved satisfactory.

Semi-permanent mounts can be made successfully by transferring the organ to be studied directly on to a micro slide and mounting it in a drop of glycerine jelly under a cover glass. However, where a more permanent preparation is desired the best mounting medium is 'Euparal Vert'. Canada balsam may also be used.

Methods: Wings

1. Remove the wings carefully from a bee and immerse them in 95% alcohol, 2 mins. or longer. Small watch glasses are useful here.

2. Transfer the wings to xylol, 2 mins.

3. Mount in 'Euparal Vert'.

Sting

1. Remove the sting from a bee either by allowing it to sting your hand or a pad of soft material such as blotting paper. If the blotting paper smells faintly of amyl acetate there will be no difficulty in getting the bee to sting it. The sting may then be scraped out of your hand or the blotting paper. Scrape out the sting rather than pull it out.
2. Transfer to 95% alcohol. About 30 mins. or so.
3. Transfer to xylol, 2 mins.
4. Mount in ' Euparal Vert '.

The various parts of the sting should be arranged spread-eagle fashion so that they may be more easily studied. This arrangement also makes the material lie fairly flat on the slide so that it can be conveniently covered by a drop of mountant, under the cover glass.

Legs

The legs and all chitinous parts of the bee are best softened before being mounted. This is easily done by soaking them in caustic soda solution (10%). Quite satisfactory preparations may be made as follows:

Method

1. Carefully remove the legs from the bee and wash them well in alcohol.
2. Transfer to caustic soda solution. Twelve to 24 hours is usually adequate.
3. Wash thoroughly in water.
4. Transfer to alcohol (95%) 2 mins.
5. Transfer to xylol. 2 mins.
6. Arrange the specimen carefully in the centre of the micro slide and apply a conveniently sized drop of mountant.
7. Finish with a cover glass and allow the preparation to set under a light weight.
8. Label.

TABLE 5

Alcohol Strengths

To Make % Alcohol	Vols. 95% Alcohol Required	Vols. Water Required
90	90	5
75	75	20
70	70	25
50	50	45
30	30	65

THE POLLEN ANALYSIS OF HONEY

It is common knowledge that honeys from different countries and from different regions of the same country show extraordinary variation.

This is due to the varied nectar yielding flora available to the bees during the active honey-gathering season. The foraging period may extend from the month of May to the beginning of September thereby covering the flowering period of a great variety of plants visited by bees.

The number of major honey yielding plants is comparatively small and because of this many honey producers claim to be able to state the source or sources of honey simply by an assessment of the flavour and aroma of a sample.

This method is, at best, rough and ready. If the source of any honey is to be determined accurately, and, if any admixture of honey-dew is to be detected, a more exact method of assessment is required.

A useful method is available in the pollen analysis of honey, i.e. the separation of the pollen grains contained in the honey, and the determination of the floral species represented.

When the worker bee visits a nectar yielding blossom it gathers up in its load of nectar a quantity of pollen belonging to the plant visited. Some of this pollen is retained in the ripened honey which is subsequently stored in the honey combs. It is thus possible to determine the origin of any honey and to a certain extent the proportions of the various nectars present.

Definition

The pollen analysis of honey may be defined as the determination of the floral source of honey by means of the pollen grains or other material found in the ' pollen spectrum ', i.e. the pollen sediment as derived from a honey sample.

Practical value

Pollen analysis provides the only reliable method of determining the geographical origin of honey. It makes possible the recognition of particular honey types and honey-dew honeys, characteristic of the region in which they were produced. Thus, an examination of the pollen spectra of different honeys allows an assessment of the most useful nectar-producing plants in any region. In other words the range and ecology of the various honey flowers exploited by the bees is reflected in the pollen spectrum.

An indication of the range of plants visited for nectar is given in Fig. 21. This shows, to a certain degree, the 'popularity' of the different species, at any rate for the year in question. Variation can, of course, be expected here since not all honey plants are regular yielders, e.g. hawthorn and lime tree.

Accuracy of pollen analysis

As already indicated pollen analysis is based on the fact that pollen grains of the plant visited by the bees are found in the nectar and consequently give a clue to the origin of the honey.

Table 6 adapted from Todd & Vansell [18] gives an indication of the vast number of pollen grains contained in one cc. of nectar from selected honey plants while Table 7 gives a pollen content comparison between hand- and bee-collected nectar from the same plants.

It must be noted, however, that not all plants yield the same amount of pollen and some idea of the variation can be obtained from Table 8.

It is, therefore, clear, that a straightforward count of pollens in a pollen spectrum may not necessarily give an absolute indication of the percentages of nectar gathered from different species. It is possible that some species may be over-represented, e.g. sweet chestnut which produces a vast number of relatively small pollen grains. On the other hand the lime tree, which appears to produce small amounts of pollen, may be under-represented. For absolute accuracy some 'corrective factor', not yet determined, may have to be applied to the straight percentage count.

A further complication arises when it is remembered that there is a constant flow of food material (honey and pollen) from the

Fig. 21

Frequency of Occurrence of Pollen from Honey Plants in 100 samples of Honey Selected at random from Apiaries in Great Britain extending from Shetland to Southern England.   Season 1950.

Frequency of Occurrence in 100 samples

	10	20	30	40	50	60	70	80	90	100
Trifolium repens										
Rubus sp.										
Acer sp.										
Brassica sp.										
Calluna vulgaris										
Crataegus sp.										
Prunus/Pyrus sp.										
Vicia sp.										
Gramineae form.										
Tilia sp.										
Chamaenerion sp.										
Aesculus sp.										
Taraxacum sp.										
Cirsium sp.										
Trifolium pratense										
Compositae form.										
Erica sp.										
Umbel type										
Fungus spores, etc.										
Centaurea sp.										
Ribes sp.										
Scabiosa sp.										
Labiatae form.										
Salix sp.										
Campanula sp.										
Ranunculus sp.										
Betula sp.										
Oxalis sp.										
Plantain sp.										
Malvaceae form.										
Filipendual sp.										
Impatiens sp.										
Lotus sp.										
Viola sp.										
Pinus sp.										
Tussilago sp.										
Agrostemma sp.										
Rumex sp.										

honey sac backwards to the ventriculus (Table 9). The extent
of this reduction may be judged from Table 10.

TABLE 6
(from Todd and Vansell)

Pollen Grains In Hand-collected Nectar

Nectar Plant	No. of Samples	Thousands of grains of pollen per c.c. nectar (means)
Robinia pseudoacacia	6	1·67±0·61
Apricot	21	6·75±0·99
Prunus domestica	110	7·09±0·57
Plum	169	10·94±0·82
Valencia orange	17	25·0 ±3·43
Willow. *Salix* sp.	13	80·0 ±1·96

TABLE 7
(from Todd and Vansell)

Comparison of Pollen Counts in Nectars Collected by Hand and by Bees

Plant source	Thousands of Pollen Grains per cc. of nectar (means)	
	Collected by hand	Collected by bees
Robinia pseudoacacia	1·67±0·61	2·67±0·62
Apricot	6·75±0·99	4·84±2·91
Prunus domestica	7·09±0·57	2·41±1·02
Plum	10·94±0·82	2·97±0·75
Valencia orange	25·0 ±3·43	6·77±0·62
Salix sp.	80·0 ±1·96	47·78±5·24

Nevertheless, careful checking of the honey flora of a locality
together with bee activity during the honey flow, and a comparison with a pollen analysis of honey gathered in the region,
does indicate that the technique is reasonably accurate. It is

assumed, of course, that the honey sample has been ' fairly ' obtained and that all possibility of the fortuitous mixing of pollen,

TABLE 8
(From Todd and Vansell)

Pollen Content of Bee-collected Nectars of some Common Honey Plants

Plant Source	No. of Samples	Thousand Grains of Pollen per cc. Nectar (means)
Willow herb. *Epilobium angustifolium*	27	0·22
Buckwheat. *Erigonium* sp.	78	1·39±0·22
Peach. *Prunus persica*	20	1·8 ±0·41
Hairy vetch	25	2·16±0·52
Prune. *Prunus domestica*	84	2·41±1·02
Milk thistle. *Silybum marianum*	37	2·92±0·59
Plum. *Prunus* sp.	29	2·97±0·75
Cherry. *Prunus avium*	111	3·95±0·51
Pear. *Pyrus communis*	37	12·30±2·28
Apple. *Pyrus malus*	75	13·80±1·73
Charlock. *Brassica*	57	21·52±2·35
Raspberry. *Rubus Ideaus*	18	21·67±1·15
Cantaurea sp.	25	24·00±3·57
Trifolium repens	56	45·00±3·62
Willow. *Salix* sp.	27	47·78±5·24
Alsike clover. *Trifolium hybr.*	46	64·78±7·13

TABLE 9
(from Todd and Vansell)

Frequency Distribution of Pollen Grains in Honey Stomach of Bees 15 *Minutes after Feeding as Compared with the Number* Immediately *after Feeding.*

Test No.	Immediately after feeding Thousands of Pollen grains	15 mins. after feeding. No. of bees in class group with indicated range in number of Pollen Grains					
		thou. 0-20	thou. 21-40	thou. 41-60	thou. 61-80	thou. 81-100	over 100
1.	184-200	2	2	0	2	0	0
2.	206-245	12	3	4	1	0	0
3.	310-338	7	2	4	2	1	6
		21	7	8	5	1	6

e.g. from occasional pollen cells, and/or wet combs from some previous honey flow or from comb breakage during extracting, is eliminated.

TABLE 10
(from Todd and Vansell)

Number of Pollen Grains in three types of food before feeding and after storage by bees.

Type of Food	Thousands of Pollen Grains per cc.	
	Before Feeding	After storage and sealing
Clear syrup	0·0	0·1
Dilute star thistle honey	5·2	1·2
Syrup and Pollen	750	253

Absolute pollen content of honey

The absolute number of pollen grains contained in honey shows considerable variation. This is, of course, due to the variability of the pollen yield from the different honey plants and again to the method of honey extraction, pressing, etc. Some honey samples may contain only a few thousand pollen grains per 10 gms. while the figure in others may be as large as 160,000. Where an exceptionally high figure is obtained it may be concluded that a certain amount of pollen has been derived from sources other than the nectary of the plant and, consequently, it is not wise to draw any definite conclusion from the pollen analysis of such a sample. A normal honey should contain between 25,000 to 60,000 pollen grains per 10 gms. (see Honey Analysis Techniques).

Honey-dew honeys

For many years the origin of honey-dew has created considerable argument among beekeepers and naturalists. While certain types of honey-dew may originate from purely plant sources, e.g. certain conifers and common laurel, it seems fairly certain that honey-dew is the sweet liquid excreted on to the foliage of a variety of plants and trees by hemipterous insects, e.g. aphids. Chemically, honey-dew may be distinguished by its property of rotating plane polarised light to the right and its high ash and dextrin content but pollen analysis affords a quick and easy way of distinguishing honey-dew honey from floral honey. The pollen spectrum of a honey-dew type honey reveals the presence of large numbers of soot or dirt particles; fragments of plant tissue; insect hairs and legs; lepidoptera wing scales; mites; fungus spores; algal cells; nematode worms; pollen of anemophilous plants such as grasses and plantain (Figs. 33 and 34).

Small nematodes are, of course, not common in honey-dew honeys but I have found them occasionally and they have also been noted by Zander [13]. It is suggested that they may be taken up by bees in drinking water since certain stages of the eelworm are passed in moist earth. It is also known that nematode worms are associated with carnivorous fungi and since spores of fungi appear to a greater or lesser degree in honey-dew honeys it is possible that the eelworms are carried to the honey storage combs in the honey-dew.

Honey-dew honeys are normally of high viscosity and dark or black in colour although occasionally if the honey-dew is of conifer origin the colour may be amber.

Another method of distinguishing honey-dew honey from floral honey is due to Mitchell.[14]

This is based on the pH value, the % ash content and the % reducing sugar of the sample. It is possible, mathematically, to derive from these three values what is known as a Discriminant Function. This is given by the equation:

$$x = -8 \cdot 3a - 12 \cdot 3b + 1 \cdot 4c$$

where $a = p$H, $b =$ % ash and $c =$ % reducing sugar. The discriminant values (means) suggested are: pure floral honeys, 86·7; honey-dew honeys, 57·6. It is suggested that any honey having a Discriminant Function greater than 73·1 can be considered to be of pure floral origin while a sample having a Discriminant Function of less than 73·1 may be considered to consist largely of honey-dew.

Preparation of 'standard' pollen slides

It is essential, if a satisfactory comparison is to be made between pollen as appearing in a pollen sediment preparation from honey and a prepared 'standard' slide, that the conditions under which the pollen is examined should be, as nearly as possible identical. The following method, complementary to that used in the preparation of pollen sediment from honey and in which the pollen grains are stained, allows the best possible comparison.

Method

1. Transfer the pollen from ripe anthers to a micro slide.
2. Remove adhering oils from the pollen by means of a drop of alcohol or ether.
3. Add a drop of ' pollen-free ' honey solution and stir in the pollen.   Pollen-free honey solution is prepared by dissolving 10 gm. honey in 20 cc. water and centrifuging out the pollen.
4. Stain with basic aqueous fuchsin.   Only a minute quantity of stain is necessary and care must be taken not to over-stain otherwise the preparation is useless.   The correct amount of stain (judged by experience) may be taken up on the tip of a thin glass rod and stirred into the honey-pollen preparation.
5. Dry on a hot plate until the preparation has a ' glazed ' appearance.
6. Apply a drop of ' Euparal Vert ' mountant and complete the preparation with a cover glass.

Preparations thus made are permanent and require no further ' ringing '.

Also, the pollen grains are presented fully expanded, exactly as they appear in honey.

Preparation of pollen sediment from honey

Apparatus required

(a) *Centrifuge.* Two or 4 bucket type taking 15 cc. tubes. A hand driven centrifuge is satisfactory but the electric, power driven pattern is more efficient.   It is best to use a centrifuge in which the buckets travel at right angles to the driving spindle. This ensures efficient deposition of the pollen sediment at the bottom of the tubes.

(b) *Gravitation Tubes.*   Where no centrifuge is available quite satisfactory results may be had by using gravitation tubes as described by Yate-Allen [15].   The gravitation method is slower than the centrifuge and not so satisfactory.

(c) *Microscope.*   Pollen analysis work demands a first class instrument.   For normal analysis work and identification of pollen types a magnification of 400 diameters is most suitable. To facilitate counting the grains the microscope should be fitted with a mechanical stage. A graticuled ocular (ruled in squares) is also useful in counting.

(*d*) *Glass slides.* Standard 3 × 1 in. type.

(*e*) *Fine-pointed forceps.*

(*f*) *Micro slide Cover Glasses.* Grade No. 2.

(*g*) *Hot Plate for slide drying.* A piece of brass 6 × 4 × $\frac{1}{8}$ in. placed on a tripod over a Bunsen burner serves admirably. The plate is heated over a low flame at one end and the slides are placed for drying at the other.

(*h*) *Beaker.* 250 cc. capacity is suitable.

(*i*) *Measuring cylinder.* 50 or 100 cc.

(*j*) *Glass stirring rod.*

(*k*) *Pipette.* A piece of 3/16 in. diameter glass tubing drawn out to a fine tip 1/32 in. diameter and fitted with a fountain pen filler rubber bulb at one end answers satisfactorily.

Stain

Basic Aqueous Fuchsin.	Basic fuchsin	0·1 gm.
	Distilled water	160 cc.
	Alcohol (70%)	1 cc.

Mounting Medium. 'Euparal Vert'. This is a proprietary mountant and is available from Messrs Flatters and Garnett, Manchester.

Method

1. Dissolve approx. 10 gms. honey in 20 cc. water (distilled).
2. Fill centrifuge tubes to the 10 cc. mark and spin in centrifuge for 1 minute at approx. 2000 r.p.m.
3. Decant into the beaker all except 0·5 cc. of the solution at the bottom of one of the tubes where the sediment has collected.
4. With the pipette take up the sediment in one of the tubes and add this to the other which becomes the 'collecting' tube.

5. From the beaker refill both tubes and repeat stages 2 to 4, until the bottom of the collecting tube is visibly covered with pollen sediment.

6. Carefully decant all the solution from the collecting tube taking care not to lose any of the sediment. If the decanting is carefully done the pollen sediment will remain suspended in a drop of honey solution at the bottom of the collecting tube.

7. Take up carefully in the pipette the drop of sediment and transfer to a cleaned 3×1 in. glass slide and, with a glass rod spread the drop over an area of approx. 1 sq. cm.

8. On the tip of a tapered glass rod take up a very small drop of stain (experience will soon dictate the correct amount) and stir this carefully among the pollen sediment on the slide.

9. Place the slide on the hot plate (the plate should, of course, not be too hot) and allow to dry until the preparation assumes a glazed appearance.

10. Remove from the hot plate and mount in a drop of ' Euparal Vert ' using a No. 2 cover glass.

This method gives a properly finished, permanent preparation and no further sealing of the cover slip is required.

Method of counting pollen grains in honey preparation

Where the pollen content of the sample is normal the grains will be distributed fairly evenly over the 1 sq. cm. area and an examination of 20 ' fields ' across the centre of the preparation will normally be sufficient to give a total count of 150 to 200 grains.

The proportions of the different floral species represented in the pollen spectrum can then be expressed as percentages.

Counting can be done either with or without a graticulated ocular at any convenient magnification, e.g. 200 diameters.

For the ' certain ' identification of some grains a magnification of 400 diameters is necessary.

As the grains are identified and counted in each field the number is entered in the species or type column as shown on page 114.

H

Method of setting out and entering up pollen counting form.
Identification Number or Mark of Honey Sample. " A "

Trifolium repens	Chamaenerion sp.	Crataegus type	Tilia sp.	Castanea sp.
10.12.12.4.6. 8.15.14.15. 8.6.2.2.	2.4.3. 2.1.2. 3.2.	1.2.1.1.1.	1.1.1. 1	4.2.1.6.4.3. 2
114	19	6	4	22
64%	11%	3·5%	2%	12·5%

Cirsium sp.	Heracleum sp.	Gramineae form.	Unidentified	Total
1.1.1. 3	1.1. 2	1.1.1.1. 4	1.1.1. 3	177
1·7%	1·6%	2%	1·7%	

A report form can be conveniently set out as follows:

Name ....

Address ....

....

....

Honey Sample

Pollen Analysis
Floral Types Represented in the Pollen Spectrum

over 45%	16-45%	1-15%

Notes

Classification of pollen grains

It is doubtful if an entirely satisfactory method of classification suitable for the honey pollen analyst can be devised but I have found the following system works well enough in practice. In devising it I have drawn freely from Faegri & Iversen [16] and Armbruster & Oenike.[17]

The method is based on:

(a) The form of the pollen grain.
(b) The size of the pollen grain.
(c) The texture of the exine of the pollen grain.
(d) The shape of the pollen grain.

Familiarity with the varied forms of pollen as it appears in honey sediment can be acquired only by the preparation of standard slides of the species most likely to be found in honey samples, and careful study of pollen grain photographs and drawings.

Zander [13] Volume 2 and Figs. 22 to 34 should prove helpful in pollen identification.

Identification of pollen grains

The identification of pollen grains in pollen spectra is difficult and skill in this technique can only be acquired after some considerable study both of ' standard ' preparations and such photographs and line drawings as are available.

It must be appreciated that identification of definite species is seldom possible since many species of the same natural order have similar pollen. For example, the pollen grains of the raspberry and those of the blackberry or bramble, are identical. The same applies to the general fruit group which, in any pollen analysis can only be indicated as *Prunus/Pyrus* sp.

Perhaps the only species that *can* be identified with any degree of certainty are *Trifolium repens*, *Trifolium pratense*, *Calluna vulgaris* and *Erica cinerea* although in this last instance I suggest it is safer to indicate the pollen merely as *Erica* sp.

It is not possible here to give morphological details of every pollen type likely to be met with in honey. All that can be attempted is the presentation of data relevant to the most useful nectar yielding plants in the British Isles, based on the pollen

Classification of Form of Pollen Grains

Type	Example	Symbol
Polyadeae	*Acacia*	Poly
Tetradeae	*Ericaceae*	Tetr.
Dyadeae	*Schouchzonia*	Dy.
Vesiculatae	*Pinus*	Ves.
Inaperturatae	*Juncaceae*	Inap.
Monoporatae	*Gramineae*	P 1.
Monocolpatae	*Liliaceae*	C 1.
Syncolpatae	*Myrtaceae, Ribes*	C Syn.
Dicolpatae	*Calla palustris*	C 2.
Tricolpatae	*Rosaceae*	C 3.
Stephanocolpatae	*Labiatae*	C Stp.
Pericolpatae	*Ranunculus*	C Peri.
Tricolporatae	*Trifolium*	
	Umbel	C 3　P 3
Stephanocolporatae	*Polygala*	C P stp.
Pericolporatae	*Rumex.*	C P peri.
Diporatae	*Colchium*	P2
Triporatae	*Tilia*	P3
Stephanoporatae	*Ulmus*	
	Alnus	P stp.
Periporatae	*Malvaceae*	P peri.
Fenestratae	*Taraxacum*	Fen.
Heterocolpatae	*Verbena*	C het.
Extraporatae	*Platycarya*	P extra.

Classification of Size of Pollen Grains

(a)　0-10 microns　　(c)　25-50 microns
(b)　10-25　do.　　(d)　50-100　do.
(e)　over 100 do.

Classification of Texture of Exine of Pollen Grains

(a)　Smooth　　　　(d)　Grooved
(b)　Granular　　　(e)　Reticular
(c)　Warty　　　　(f)　Spiny
(g)　Pitted

Classification of Shape of Pollen Grains

(a)　Triangular　　　(e)　Pentagonal
(b)　Spherical　　　(f)　Tetrahedral
(c)　Oval　　　　　(g)　Rhomboidal
(d)　Rectangular　　(h)　Crescent

analysis of 855 samples of honey (Table 11), and a few of the most common pollen grains found in Australian and New Zealand honey (see photographic illustrations, Figs. 22-34).

TABLE 11

Plant and Pollen Data

Plant	Type	Size in microns	Texture	Shape
Trifolium repens	C3 P3	23·1 × 19·8	Granular	Oval
Prunus/Pyrus sp.	C3	40·8	Granular	Triangular
Rubus sp.	C3	23·8	Smooth	Triangular
Acer sp.	C3	30·6	Smooth	Triangular
Castanea sp.	C3 P3	13·2 × 9·9	Smooth	Oval
Tilia sp.	P3	28·9	Smooth	Spherical
Brassica sp.	C3 P3	27·2	Reticular	Spherical
Ligustrum sp.	C3 P3	23·8	Reticular	Spherical
Vicia sp.	C3 P3	33·0 × 19·8	Granular	Rectangular
Trifolium pratense	C3 P3	30·6	Reticular	Spherical
Chamaenerion sp.	P3	54·4	Granular	Spherical
Cirsium sp.	C3 P3	37·4	Spiny	Spherical
Campanula sp.	P peri.	28·9	Spiny	Spherical
Calluna vulgaris	Tetr.	34·0 × 40·0	Granular	Rhomboidal
do. do.	do.	34·0	Granular	Tetrahedral
Hercaleum sp.	C3 P3	33·0 × 16·5	Granular	Rectangular
Taraxacum sp.	Fen.	23·8	Spiny	Spherical
Centaurea sp.	C3 P3	28·9	Spiny	Spherical
Aesculus sp.	C3 P3	20·4 × 17·0	Smooth	Oval
Erica sp.	Tetr.	44·2	Smooth	Tetrahedral
Labiatae sp.	C Stp.	27·2	Granular	Spherical
Viola sp.	C5 P5	56·0 × 62·5	Granular	Pentagonal
Most Common types of Pollen Grains found in Australian and New Zealand honey				
Myrtaceae sp.	C Syn.	13·6 × 17·0	Smooth	Triangular
Acacia sp.	Poly.	34·0 × 40·8	Smooth	Rhomboidal
Echium sp.	P3	17·0 × 18·7	Smooth	Oval
Banksia sp.	P2	44·2 × 20·4	Granular	Crescent

HONEY ANALYSIS

Before considering the technique of honey analysis it will be useful to review briefly the nature of honey and its composition.

Honey has been described as ' bottled sunshine ' and there is, in fact, quite a measure of truth in this idea.

The raw material out of which the bees produce their honey is known as nectar. Nectar is a sweet, watery liquid, containing from 30% to 70% moisture. In order to attract the attention of the pollinating insect, essential for the continuance of the species, the flower possesses colour, aroma and sweetness and it is the elaboration of sugar that is, first of all, exploited by the bee and, in turn, the beekeeper.

The composition of nectar sugars has been studied in detail by Percival [21] who distinguishes 10 different types of nectar. Some have sucrose as the dominant sugar, others are balanced, containing about equal parts sucrose, fructose and glucose while in a third group fructose and glucose are dominant.

It seems that sucrose dominated nectars are associated with long tubed flowers which possess a protected nectary and fructose plus glucose dominated nectars with ' open ' flowers possessing unprotected nectaries.

It is interesting that white clover, the most important nectar source in Britain has a sucrose dominant nectar.

In the field, bees do not appear to show any preference for a particular nectar type.

According to Jaeger [29] the concentration of nectar varies considerably: dry weight values ranging from 8·2% in Fritillary, to 66·8% in horse chestnut and 76% in marjoram. The total amount of sugar contained over a period of 24 hours likewise varies with different nectars and the following values are given:

Tilia vulgaris	2·7 mg.
Trifolium pratense	0·076 mg.
Medicago sativa	0·070 mg.

Brassica napus	0·3 to 0·5 mg.
Phacelia tanacetifolia	1·0 to 2·0 mg.
Vicia faba	4·15 mg.
Pear tree	0·20 to 0·30 mg.
Wild cherry	0·47 mg.
Plum	0·41 to 0·79 mg.
Peach	2·12 mg.

The secretion of nectar varies according to the time of day greatest amounts being produced around 5 a.m. falling to a minimum about 3 p.m. and increasing again in early evening.

The term sugar is, of course, a loose one since many different types of sugar may be elaborated by a plant. Sugar chemistry is, however, a complex subject and only those sugars associated with honey will be discussed here.

We say that sugar belongs to a class of organic compounds known as carbohydrates. They are so called because they contain the elements carbon, hydrogen and oxygen; the hydrogen and oxygen being present in the same proportions as they appear in water. The compound may be represented thus : $C_x(H_2O)_y$: in other words they are hydrates of carbon. Accordingly the common sugars have the following formulae:

Glucose $C_6H_{12}O_6$
Sucrose $C_{12}H_{22}O_{11}$
Starch $(C_6H_{10}O_5)_n$ where n may be a number of the order of 50 to 100.

The vast number of carbohydrates that are known are grouped according to the number of 'sugar units' they contain. For example, sugars such as glucose and fructose are known as monosaccharides and are represented by the formula $C_6H_{12}O_6$.

Disaccharides such as sucrose, maltose, and lactose by $C_{12}H_{22}O_{11}$.

Trisaccharides such as raffinose by $C_{18}H_{32}O_{16}$.

Polysaccharides such as starch, dextrin, glycogen and cellulose by $(C_6H_{10}O_5)_n$.

Glucose (also known as dextrose) and fructose (also known as laevulose) are formed in sweet fruits such as grapes and figs and, of course, they also occur in large amounts in honey.

Sucrose or cane sugar is our common table sugar and occurs in sugar cane, sugar beet, sugar maple and other plants. Sucrose may be split up into a monosaccharide known as ' invert ' sugar by boiling with dilute acid, or, by treatment with an appropriate enzyme. The worker bee is able to secrete the enzyme ' invertase ' which it adds to whatever sweet liquid it sucks up and carries back to the hive. Bees can thus change the disaccharide sucrose into the monosaccharide invert sugar.

Maltose or malt sugar is formed by the action of the ferment diastase on starch, and, in turn, *it* breaks down to give glucose.

Dextrin (which may occur in honey-dew honey particularly) is a form of starch and is prepared by heating starch with nitric acid. It is a sticky substance and is used under the name of ' British Gum '.

Glycogen is animal or liver starch and is found in the liver of animals. It is the form in which carbohydrate is stored in that organ.

The term sugar is applied to those carbohydrates which are sweet to the taste: in honey the most commonly found are dextrose, laevulose, sucrose and maltose. These sugars differ from one another in physical and chemical properties (Table 12) and it is these differences that are made use of in their identification by the analytical techniques described later.

Plants are able to absorb water from the soil and carbon dioxide from the air and can thus produce carbohydrates.

Such a reaction does not occur automatically since it is dependent on two important factors: (*a*) the energy of sunlight, and (*b*) the catalytic action of the green colouring matter in plants known as chlorophyll. This process of putting together water and carbon dioxide under the influence of sunlight and chlorophyll is known as photosynthesis. The equation may be stated thus:

$$6\ H_2O + 6\ CO_2 = C_6H_{12}O_6 + 6\ O_2$$

water　　carbon　　　glucose　oxygen
　　　　　dioxide

For a full understanding of the nature of honey it is essential to note that laevulose and dextrose have the same empirical formulae: and, in the same way, sucrose and maltose have similar

PHOTOGRAPHIC ILLUSTRATIONS OF POLLEN GRAINS

The photographic illustrations have been taken from actual pollen spectra prepared from honey samples and do not present the grains in any idealised form. The magnification in each case is approximately × 200.

In a standard preparation it is found that the pollen grains do not all lie in the same plane, hence in the photographs some grains are out of focus. However, in each illustration the intention has been to present at least one pollen grain sharply depicted.

It should be noted that a photograph represents, in this case, an optical cross section of the pollen grain.

In most instances photographs of ' groups ' of pollen grains are shown. This plan has the advantage of showing the various pollens as they appear, or may appear, in association with each other according to the source of honey.

Pollen grains are, of course, three dimensional being either spherical or almost cylindrical with the result that when photographed as they lie in the medium of the preparation, one surface, or part of the surface, may be in focus while the remainder is out of focus.

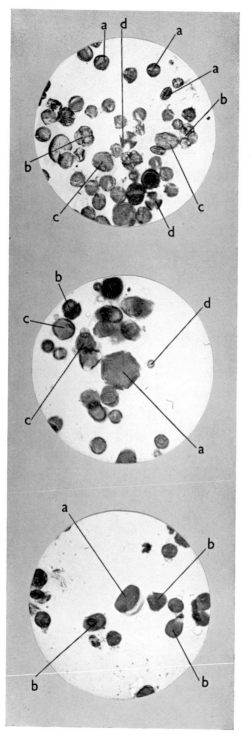

FIG. 22
a) *Trifolium repens*
b) *Calluna vulgaris*
c) *Vicia* sp.
d) *Brassica* sp.

FIG. 23
a) *Viola* sp.
b) *Brassica* sp.
c) *Trifolium pratense*
d) *Castanea* sp.

FIG. 24
a) *Liliaceae* form
b) *Rubus* sp.

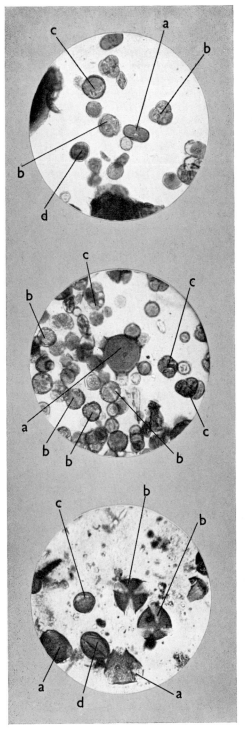

FIG. 25

a) *Heracleum* sp.
b) *Calluna vulgaris*
c) *Centaurea* sp.
d) *Trifolium repens*

FIG. 26

a) *Chamaenerion* sp.
b) *Centaurea* sp.
c) *Calluna vulgaris*

FIG. 27

a) *Prunus/Pyrus* sp.
b) *Acer* sp.
c) *Trifolium repens*
d) unexpended *Acer* sp.

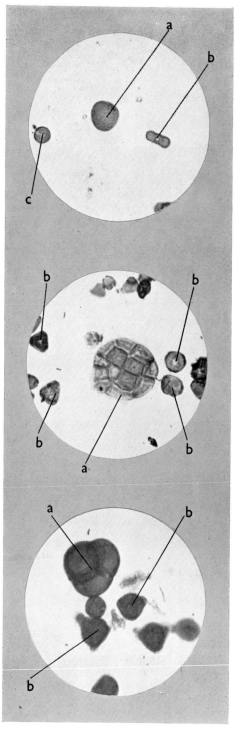

Fig. 28
a) *Tilia* sp.
b) *Heracleum* sp.
c) *Trifolium repens*

Fig. 29
a) *Acacia* sp.
b) *Myrtaceae* sp.

Fig. 30
a) *Erica* sp.
b) *Trifolium repens*

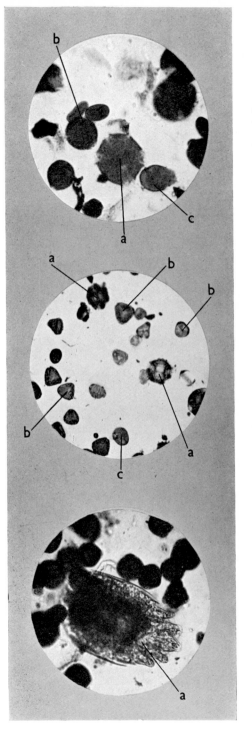

Fig. 31
a) *Labiatea* form
b) Fungus spore
c) *Acer* sp.

Fig. 32
a) *Taraxacum* sp.
b) *Myrtaceae* sp.
c) *Echium* sp.

Fig. 33
a) Mite from honey-dew honey

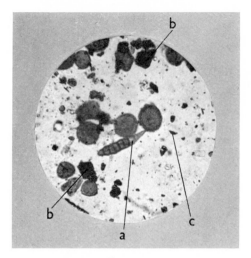

Fig. 34

a) Fungus spore
b) Soot particle
c) Background of plant debris

empirical formulae. Although the empirical formulae are similar
in these respective instances the sugars differ constitutionally.

When the chemist talks of the empirical formula of a substance
he refers only to the number of different atoms forming the molecule. Several substances possessing different properties may, in

TABLE 12

Sugar	Formula	Melting Point	Solubility	Rotation	Reduces Fehling's	Hydrolises to
Dextrose	$C_6H_{12}O_6$	145° C.	Water Alcohol	Right handed	+	—
Laevulose	$C_6H_{12}O_6$	95° C.	Water	Left handed	+	—
Sucrose	$C_{12}H_{22}O_{11}$	160° C.	Water	Right handed	—	Dextrose + Laevulose
Maltose	$C_{12}H_{22}O_{11}$	100° C.	Water	Right handed	+	Glucose

fact, have the same number of atoms making up their molecules.
The chemist therefore, also uses what he terms constitutional
formulae. Such formulae show precisely how the atoms are
arranged in the molecule. To take a very simple example: the
gas methane has the empirical formula CH_4: the constitutional
formula for the same substance is, however, set out graphically
as:

$$H-\overset{\displaystyle H}{\underset{\displaystyle H}{\overset{|}{\underset{|}{C}}}}-H$$

This indicates that the hydrogen atoms are arranged around
the carbon atom which has, as it were, four arms, conveniently
arranged to receive them.

Dextrose and laevulose differ constitutionally, and it is the
arrangement of the atoms in the molecules that accounts, in part,
for the different properties of the two sugars.

Although empirically the same and both tasting sweet, dextrose in solution has the property of turning plane polarised light to the right (hence the name dextrose): laevulose rotates such polarised light to the left (hence laevulose). See note on polarised light.

Another carbohydrate which may appear in heather honey and in honey-dew honey is of interest; this is dextrin.

Dextrin is an intermediate substance formed in the production of sugar from starch and has the formula $(C_6H_{10}O_5)_n$.

There is some evidence that the presence of dextrin in honey on which bees are wintering is harmful in that such winter food is not easily digested. This difficulty in making full use of winter stores appears to set up some excitement which results in the colony developing dysentery during the late winter and early spring.

Where bees are wintering on *pure* heather honey there is usually no difficulty but if the heather honey is mixed with honey from some other source, such as clover, colonies frequently winter badly.

Honey sugars

The sugars normally found in honey are dextrose, laevulose and maltose. At one time it was thought that cane sugar was a normal constituent of honey but modern analytical techniques, particularly that of paper partition chromatography, show that cane sugar is not normally present.

A number of sugars may be found in honey and the most recent work (White [26]) indicates that the following have been identified.

> *Monosaccharides.* Dextrose: laevulose
> *Disaccharides.* Maltose: Sucrose: Isomaltose: Turanose:
> Maltulose: Nigerose: Kojibiose.
> *Higher Sugars.* Melezitose: Erlose: Kestose: Raffinose:
> Dextrantriose.

It must not be assumed that any given sample of honey will contain all these sugars since honey, as a commodity, is extremely variable, according to local flora and season.

Average values, covering honeys gathered in 1956 are given in Table 13, while Table 14 presents results of chromatographic analyses covering samples gathered during the 1957 season.

TABLE 13

Results of Honey Analyses Carried out in 1956

No. of Samples Examined	% Invert Sugar mean value	% Dextrose mean value	% Laevulose mean value	Specific Gravity at 60° F. mean value	pH mean value	Free Acid ml. O.I.N.NaOH per 100 gm. Honey mean value	No. of Pollen Grains per 10 gm. mean value in 1000s
57				1·412±·01			
41	68·9±4·8	34·0±2·8	35·0±2·9				
39					4·3±0·5		
36						21·5±9·5	160

TABLE 14

Results of Chromatographic Analyses of 1957 Season Honey Samples

No. of Samples Examined	No. of Samples containing Dextrose	No. of Samples containing Laevulose	No. of Samples containing Sucrose	No. of Samples containing Maltose	No. of Samples containing rare sugars
27	27	27	6	27	7

TABLE 15

Analyses of typical types of honey from Aberdeenshire

	Clover	Heather	Honey-dew
Colour	pale straw	amber	dark amber
Air bubble	none	large	very small
Refractometric Equivalents			
Refractive Index 20°C.	1·4940	1·4781	1·4885
Moisture (%)	17·4	23·4	19·2
Specific Gravity 60°F.	1·424	1·380	1·412
non-Reducing Sugar (%)	0·0	1·3	0·0
Invert sugar (%)	70·1	65·3	68·03
Dextrose (%)	32·4	30·0	33·6
Laevulose (%)	37·7	35·3	34·43
L/D Ratio	1·18	1·2	1·02
Free acid ml. 0·1			
NaOH per 100 gm. Honey	11·0	21·0	29·0
pH	4·3	4·9	4·4
Ash (%)	0·07	0·8	0·6
Colloid (%)	——	2·9	2·64
Protein (%)	——	1·8	1·4
Pollen content per 10 gm.	34,500	28,000	46,750

Pollen Analyses

Honey Type: Clover

over 45%	16-45%	1-15%
Trifolium repens 98%	——	*Lotus* sp. *Ranunculus* sp. *Trifolium pratense* *Taraxacum* type Unidentified 2%

Honey Type: Heather

over 45%	16-45%	1-15%
Calluna vulgaris 99%	——	*Erica* sp. *Trifolium repens* 1%

Honey Type: Honey-dew

over 45%	16-45%	1-15%
——	*Trifolium repens* 43% *Calluna vulgaris* 32% *Rubus* sp. 20%	*Erica* sp. *Trifolium pratense* *Acer* sp. 5%

The average composition of American honeys harvested during the 1956 and 1957 seasons are given in Table 16.

Detailed analyses of three typical Aberdeenshire honey types are presented in Table 15. It will be noted that here, evidence in support of a precise definition of honey type is offered by the pollen spectra.

TABLE 16

Average Composition of American Honey Samples (from White)

	1956 (182 samples)	1957 (297 samples)
Moisture (%)	17·0	17·3
Laevulose (%)	37·92	38·36
Dextrose (%)	31·15	31·37
Sucrose (%)	1·32	1·31
Maltose (%)	7·44	7·22
Higher sugars (%)	1·69	1·38
Undetermined (%)	3·4	2·9
pH	3·96	3·88
Free acidity (meq/kg.)	22·16	21·95
Lactone (meq/kg.)	7·05	7·15
Total acid (meq/kg.)	29·21	29·1
Lactone/Free acid	0·336	0·334
Ash (%)	0·173	0·166
Nitrogen (%)	0·041	0·041

Crystallisation

After a period of time the dextrose in honey tends to crystallise out but the laevulose remains permanently in solution. Different honey types behave differently so far as crystallisation (or granulation) is concerned, some nectar sources giving a honey that crystallises rapidly while others allow the bees to elaborate a honey type that may remain in the liquid state for up to 2 years or more.

The precise factors which affect the rate of granulation are not fully known but the L/D ratio (laevulose to dextrose) and the colloid content appear to have some influence.

The texture or ' grain ' of the granulation is dependent largely on the rate of granulation and the moisture content. If a honey crystallises rapidly, i.e. within some days or a week or two, the texture is always fine and lardlike, the crystals being of very small size. On the other hand where a sample takes some months or even years to granulate, e.g. honey of low water content or high colloid content, the crystals are large and the texture coarse.

Where a market exists for finely granulated honey crystallisation may be accelerated artificially by the addition to the liquid honey of a small quantity of granulated honey and the mixture agitated at regular intervals (see Honey Production Techniques.)

A peculiarity of granulation occurs where a certain amount of the honey crystallises in white, cauliflower-like masses, usually near or at the surface of the container: this is known as ' frosting '. Dextrose may crystallise out as (a) a hydrate, or (b), in the anhydrous form and when anhydrous crystallisation occurs the honey takes on the characteristic frosted appearance.

Fermentation

Honey always contains yeasts which are said to be ' sugar tolerant ' and, so long as conditions are unsuitable for their growth, they cause no harm. If, however, the water content of the honey is high or if it is allowed to increase, i.e. through faulty storage in a damp atmosphere, these yeasts become active and begin to ' work '.

The result is that fermentation of the honey gets under way and it is rapidly spoiled. Fermentation is brought about by the enzyme zymase as follows:

$$C_6H_{12}O_6 + zymase = 2 \ C_2H_5OH + 2 \ CO_2$$

sugar   zymase   alcohol carbon dioxide

The fact that honey is easily fermented may be put to practical use in the making of mead.

If the original specific gravity of any honey sample is of the order of 1·410 at 60° F. or lower, fermentation is likely to occur within 1 to 2 months after storage. Again, if the water content of a sample tends to be high, and the honey crystallises, fermentation usually sets in. Fermentation of crystallised honey is, to begin with, confined to the upper layers but it soon spreads throughout the mass. Fermentation may be stopped, provided it has not gone too far, if the honey is heated to a temperature of about 150° F., maintained at that figure for approximately 30 minutes and then allowed to cool. If a quantity of honey is to be stored for some months or more and the specific gravity at 60° F. is 1·410 or less, it is advisable to heat it as noted above in order to prevent the development of the yeasts. These yeasts are of course, always present in the air and cannot be avoided unless the honey is handled in a sterile atmosphere. Indeed, sometimes they may be present in the original nectar, so fermentation must, at all times, be considered a risk where honey of low specific gravity is being stored.

It must, of course, be understood that to heat honey at all is bad practice since much of its fragrance will be destroyed: and there is always a danger that it may become partially if not wholly carmelised.

When heating honey the lid of the container should be kept on, securely. If this point is not noted the honey will again lose its fragrance owing to the loss, through evaporation, of the essential oils which characterise it.

Where sound beekeeping methods are practised there will be no danger of any sample of honey being of specific gravity lower than 1·410 at 60° F., but if at any time the honeycombs are extracted before they are completely sealed over there is a danger that the water content will be higher than normal with the subsequent risk of fermentation. The critical water content is 19·4%, i.e. a specific gravity of 1·410 at 60° F.

A point of practical importance to note is that honey is hygroscopic, i.e. it has the property of absorbing water vapour from the air. If honey is exposed to the air it tends to establish an equilibrium in moisture content with that of the atmosphere. This takes place very rapidly to begin with, then more slowly as equilibrium is reached. Normally, in the British Isles, the less honey is exposed to the air, the better, a point which must be noted when handling the honey crop in the process of extracting and bottling.

This moisture exchange can also occur through the wax capping of the honey comb so that if honey combs are to be stored for any time prior to extraction the environmental atmosphere should be as dry as possible.

Over the British Isles the average specific gravity of honey, from year to year, is of the order of 1·415 at 60° F. with a Standard

Deviation (see Statistical Techniques) of $\pm 0 \cdot 009$. This means that 66% of all samples vary, in specific gravity from $1 \cdot 424$ to $1 \cdot 406$ at $60°$ F. i.e. the moisture content varies from $17 \cdot 4\%$ to 20%.

Heather honey is, however, the exception so far as water content is concerned since the moisture present in this type of honey may be of the order of 23% without giving any cause for alarm. The reason for this is that the colloid content of heather honey is high and this fact to a large extent offsets the danger of fermentation due to the high moisture percentage. Nevertheless heather honey is prone to fermentation especially if it is not absolutely pure. It seems that any admixture of clover honey with the ling heather honey tends to ferment readily and may, in practice cause quite a bit of trouble where colonies have been working on both honey sources. Such trouble arises in late winter or early spring when there may be signs of unrest in the colony followed by a certain amount of dysentery.

In beekeeping practice large quantities of sugar syrup are fed to bees mainly for spring and autumn stores. The worker bees alter, chemically, this sugar, i.e. they 'invert' it and elaborate invert sugar consisting of equal parts dextrose and laevulose as follows:

$$C_{12}H_{22}O_{11} + H_2O = C_6H_{12}O_6 + C_6H_{12}O_6$$
cane sugar   water   dextrose   laevulose

As has been noted above, heather honey, i.e. honey from the ling heather (*Calluna vulgaris*) is different from honey from practically all other flowers.

Unlike other honey types it does not flow: it is gelatinous in character and, when in the liquid state, a jar containing ling honey may be inverted without the honey showing any movement. This is, in fact, one test for the purity of a sample of ling heather honey. Because of the gelatinous nature of such honey the air bubbles, arising from the pressing of the honey from the comb, become trapped in the mass and heather honey is characterised by the presence of these air bubbles. The size of air bubble can be taken to be a fairly good guide to the purity of the honey. Heather honey possesses the property of thixotropy, i.e. when the gel form is agitated it becomes liquid, for a time, returning

I

again to the gel state. This fact is made use of in some methods of obtaining heather honey from the comb, when, after agitation, the heather honey combs may be extracted in the same manner as clover or other non-thixotropic honeys. Such a method of heather honey extraction is not, however, very efficient.

In the analysis of heather honey reference is sometimes made to the thixotropy ratio. This is determined by means of a viscometer. This instrument consists of a glass tube of about 1 inch diameter, open at one end. The honey is poured into the tube and allowed to stand for 24 hours. A steel ball of 0·25 inch diameter is then introduced and its rate of fall timed over a distance of 14 cm. The honey is now stirred and a second ball introduced, and again timed for rate of fall over the same distance. The ratio between the two readings is known as the thixotropy ratio.

The thixotropy ratio, e.g. for clover honey would be unity and for good quality ling heather honey, 100.

Note on polarised light

Light, i.e. light from the sun, an electric bulb or similar source is said to travel in waves which vibrate in an infinite number of planes at right angles to the path along which the light is travelling. When such light is polarised it is said to vibrate in only one transverse plane.

Certain substances e.g. Iceland Spar (calcite) and a material known as ' polaroid ' possess the property of arresting the infinite number of planes of vibration and allowing the light to pass in *one* plane only. Such light is said to be plane polarised. Light falling on glass at a certain angle is also plane polarised, and light reflected from blue sky may be largely polarised.

The human eye, of course, cannot detect plane polarised light but, if polaroid spectacles are worn, glare from any surface reflecting polarised or partly polarised light is considerably reduced. In photography, troublesome reflections from a highly polished surface may be overcome by means of a polarising filter placed over the camera lens.

Plane polarised light on emerging from a suitably prepared piece of calcite may be accepted or rejected by a similar piece of Iceland Spar. If accepted the light will continue on its way; if rejected, the human eye perceives nothing but a black area.

The second piece of spar, called an analyser, when set at a given angle will accept completely the plane polarised light but when turned through an angle of 90 degrees will reject or block, completely, the same light. If the analyser is rotated so that its plane of polarisation is not exactly at right angles to that of the polariser a proportional amount of light will be allowed to pass (Fig. 35).

Certain sugars possess the property of rotating the plane of polarised light, either to left or right (they may be designated right handed and left handed sugars) and the angle through which the plane polarised light is rotated is specific for the various sugars. This property may be made use of in sugar analysis, the instrument devised for the technique being called a saccharimeter.

Honey, although a combination of sugars, normally rotates polarised light to the left. However, honey-dew honey and honey containing excess, i.e. 10% or so of cane sugar, will rotate the plane of polarisation to the right.

The techniques involved in saccharimetry will not be discussed here.

Determination of invert sugar in honey

The following volumetric method makes use of Fehling's solution and gives reasonably accurate results.

Fehling's solution: There are many mixtures of copper sulphate, tartaric acid salts and alkalis used by chemists in the determination of reducing sugars but the most widely adopted is that of Fehling.

Fehling's solution is made up in two separate parts as follows:

Solution 'A': Pure copper sulphate 34·639 gms. is dissolved in water and diluted to exactly 500 cc.
Solution 'B': Rochelle salts 173 gms. Sodium hydroxide 50 gms. Dissolve in water and dilute to exactly 500 cc.

For use the Fehling's solution is prepared by taking 5 cc. each of solutions 'A' and 'B'.

The solution must be standardised against a 0·05% solution of pure, anhydrous dextrose in water: 10 cc. of this dextrose solution should reduce, exactly, the copper in 10 cc. Fehling's solution.

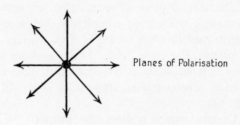

Planes of Polarisation

When polarised the effect is thus:-

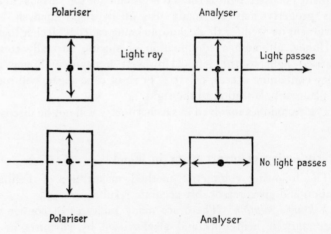

FIG. 35. LOOKING DOWN A RAY OF LIGHT

When planes of vibration are the same, light passes : when planes of vibration are at right angles to one another, no light is allowed to pass.

Reagents Required.   (*a*) Fehling's solution.

                           (*b*) 1% aqueous soln. methylene blue.

Method

1. Weigh accurately 0·3 gm. honey in a 250 cc. beaker.
2. Add 100 cc. distilled water and stir until the honey has dissolved.

3. Prepare 10 cc. Fehling's soln. (5 cc. ' A ' and 5 cc. ' B ') and add about 40 cc. distilled water.

4. Boil the Fehling's soln. and, while still boiling run the sugar, i.e. the honey soln., into the flask from a burette. The sugar soln. reduces the Fehling's soln. and a brick red precipitate of cuprous oxide is formed. Boiling should continue for about 2 minutes after each addition of honey soln. (The term ' reduction ' means the removal of oxygen from a substance, or, owing to the opposite chemical nature of hydrogen, the addition of hydrogen.)

5. The end point of the titration is determined by adding two drops of 1% aqueous soln. of methylene blue to the boiling Fehling's soln. When reduction is complete the blue colour disappears and the liquid boils clear.

Three titrations should be run and they must agree within 0·1 cc.

Calculation: Example

10 cc. Fehling's soln. are equivalent to 0·05 gm. invert sugar.

From the titration 20·5 cc. sugar soln. are reduced by 10 cc. Fehling's soln. which has been standardised so that 10 cc. Fehling's equals 0·05 gm. invert sugar.

100 cc. honey soln. contains 0·3 gm.
20·5 cc.   „   „   0·615 gm.
20·5 cc. are equivalent to 0·05 gm. invert sugar.

$$\% \text{ invert sugar in sample } \frac{0·05 \times 100}{0·0615}$$

$$=81·3\%$$

Determination of dextrose in honey

The following method is based on the oxidation of dextrose by iodine to gluconic acid. The reaction is specific for aldoses and is thus suitable for use with honey where other sugars may be present.

In this method a blank test is run with the sodium hydroxide soln. and the difference between the two titrations calculated as dextrose. 1 cc. 0·1 N iodine is equivalent to 0·00901 gm. dextrose.

Reagents Required.   (*a*) N/10 iodine soln.
                   (*b*) N/10 sodium hydroxide soln.
                   (*c*) N/10 sodium thiosulphate soln.
                   (*d*) Starch soln.

Method

1. Dissolve 0·6 gm. honey in 20 cc. distilled water.
2. Take 5 cc. honey soln. in a 250 cc. beaker.
3. Add 10 cc. N/10 iodine soln.
4. Add 15 cc. N/10 sodium hydroxide soln.
5. Allow to stand for 15 to 20 minutes.
6. Titrate against N/10 $Na_2 S_2 O_3$. Iodine acts as its own indicator but it is an advantage to add a little starch soln. when near the end point in order to obtain greater precision in its determination.
7. Three titrations must be run and they should agree within 0·1 cc.
8. Run a blank test.

Calculation: Example

(*a*) Blank Test. No. of cc. N/10 $Na_2S_2O_3$ required to neutralise N/10 iodine-NaOH soln. 10

(*b*) Honey soln. No. of cc. N/10 $Na_2S_2O_3$ required to neutralise honey/iodine/NaOH soln. ....4·2

Difference in titrations ....5·8 cc.

1 cc. N/10 iodine soln.   0·00901 gm. dextrose.

5·8 cc. N/10 iodine soln.   0·052258 gm. dextrose.

5 cc. honey soln. contain 0·15 gm. honey.

$$\% \text{ dextrose} \frac{0·052258 \times 100}{0·15}$$

$$34·8\%$$

Determination of colloid content of honey

Reagent Required. Trichloro-acetic-acid.

The colloid content of honey varies according to the nectar source. In general, light coloured honeys contain little colloidal matter while dark coloured types and in particular honey-dew and ling heather honey normally contain upwards of 2%. My own analyses have given values of up to 6%. It has been shown by Mitchell, Irvine and Scoular [22] that approximately $\frac{2}{3}$ of the colloidal matter in honey is protein.

Colloidal particles are relatively large and while they cannot be seen readily with the optical microscope they may be seen and studied easily by means of the electron microscope. Milum [25] has indicated that ' colloids represent a state of subdivision which is intermediate between materials in solution and those in suspensions in which the particle size is not large enough to settle readily '. In other words, the colloidal material is, as it were, just ready to be precipitated out of solution and such settling out may be brought about if honey is overheated. For example, brilliantly clear clover honey when subjected to overheating, i.e. heating above 150° F. for more than one hour, may lose its sparkle and become cloudy as a result of a certain amount of colloid precipitation.

Method

1. Dissolve 20 gm. honey in 50 cc. distilled water.
2. Add 25 cc. trichloro-acetic-acid.
3. Heat and stir (2 to 3 minutes).
4. Allow precipitate to settle (48 hours).
5. Filter on dry, tared, filter paper.
6. Wash.
7. Dry to constant weight and express result as %.

Determination of the total acid in honey expressed as the mg. equivalent

Reagents required.   (a) 0·1 N NaOH
(b) phenolphthalein.

Method

1. Dissolve 10 gm. honey in 50 cc. distilled water.
2. Titrate against 0·1 N NaOH using phenolphthalein as indicator.
3. The cc. value obtained gives the quantity of 0·1 N NaOH required to neutralise the acid in 10 gm. honey. This value is known as the milligram equivalent.

Note: In using this method some practice will be required in order to determine accurately the end point of the titration especially where the honey is of a dark colour.

Determination of ash in honey

Mineral matter associated with honey is contained in the ash.   Normally, dark coloured honey types contain more ash than light coloured forms.   Ash may contain silica, iron, copper, manganese, chlorine, calcium, potassium, sodium, phosphorus, sulphur, aluminium and magnesium.   High ash content of dark honey is associated with high pH value.

Reagent required.   Conc. sulphuric acid.

Method

1. Weigh accurately 10 gm. honey in a tared silica crucible.
2. Add about 2 cc. conc. sulphuric acid.
3. Heat (carefully) until only a white ash remains.
4. Cool (in dessicator).
5. Re-weigh and express result as %.

Determination of non-reducing sugar in honey

Reagents Required.   (*a*) Fehling's soln.
  (*b*) 1% soln. methylene blue.
  (*c*) N Hydrochloric acid.

Method

1. Weigh accurately 0·3 gm. honey in a 250 cc. beaker.
2. Dissolve in 100 cc. distilled water.
3. Add 1 cc. N HCl and heat for 45 minutes in a boiling water bath.
4. Allow to cool and almost, but not quite, neutralise with N NaOH soln. (the final soln. should remain slightly acid).
5. Estimate the reducing sugar as in the determination of invert sugar.
6. The difference between the value obtained and that obtained for invert sugar is taken as non-reducing sugar.

Determination of the absolute number of pollen grains in honey

Method

1. Weigh accurately in a 250 cc. beaker 10 gm. honey.
2. Add 20 cc. distilled water and stir until all the honey has dissolved. Gentle heat may be applied if necessary.
3. Centrifuge until all the pollen has been collected in one of the graduated centrifuge tubes (see Technique of Pollen Analysis).
4. Carefully draw off the liquid, with a pipette, down to the 0·1 cc. mark. Care must be taken not to disturb the sediment at the bottom of the tube.
5. Distribute, by stirring, the sediment evenly through the honey soln. in the tube and transfer, by means of a pipette, to a haemocytometer counting chamber (the type I use is a 'Zappert' 0·100 mm.).
6. Apply a cover glass and count the number of pollen grains in 400 squares. Three groups of 400 squares should be counted and the mean value accepted.
7. The total number of grains is calculated by the following formula:

$$\text{Total no.} = \frac{D \times N}{S \times K}$$

where: D = rate of dilution
N = number of grains counted
K = constant for each small square ($1/4000$)
S = number of squares counted.

8. Using the above method and assuming a mean count of 32 grains the total number of pollen grains is conveniently given, in thousands, by the count value.

e.g. where:

$$D = 100$$
$$N = 32$$
$$K = 1/4000$$
$$S = 400$$

we have $\dfrac{100 \times 32}{400 \times 1/4000}$

$$= 32,000.$$

Determination of pH of honey

The concept of pH in relation to acid and alkaline solutions depends upon complex electro-chemical considerations. The chemist has devised the pH scale in order to describe precisely the degree of acidity or alkalinity of any given solution.

It may be taken that the pH value gives information with regard to the intensity of acidity or alkalinity. A scale of values ranging from o to 14 has been adopted, the neutral point in the scale having a value of 7, as follows:

neutrality

|

o 1 2 3 4 5 6 7 8 9 10 11 12 13 14

←———————————   ——————————→

acidity increases   alkalinity increases

In general terms it may be stated that the lower the pH value obtained for honey, the milder the flavour. Heather honey and honey-dew honey types may give pH values of around 4·0 to 5·6 and it is usual to associate a definite ' tang ' or ' bite ' with such honey. Higher pH values are normally associated with darker coloured honeys.

In honey, pH values may be determined conveniently by means of indicators. Various indicators cover different pH ranges the most convenient, so far as honey is concerned being:

Indicator	pH Range	Colour Range
Bromo-phenol Blue	2·8-4·4	yellow to purple
Bromo-cresol Green	3·6-5·2	yellow to blue
Methyl-Red	4·4-6·0	red to orange

As the pH alters, the colour of the indicator changes. Thus, comparison of the colour given by an indicator with a known standard allows us to determine the pH value.

A useful outfit, made by the British Drug Houses Ltd., makes the pH determination of honey, a simple matter.

Method

1. Dissolve 10 gm. honey in 50 cc. distilled water.
2. Using the outfit make a micro-pipette.

3. Fill the pipette to a distance of 1 inch with the selected indicator soln. and transfer to a small watch glass.
4. Take up the same amount of honey soln. without rinsing the pipette and transfer to the watch glass.
5. Refill the tube with the mixed watch glass contents and match the colour with one of the standards provided.
6. Read the pH value opposite the matched standard.

Note: It is convenient to determine the pH value then proceed directly to the determination of the total acid.

Determination of water content, specific gravity and refractive index of honey

This is most easily done by means of an instrument known as a refractometer. Within the normal limits applicable to honey there is a direct relationship between the refractive index and water content of honey, and tables, originally worked out by Chataway [23] and revised by Wedmore [44] make moisture determination a relatively simple matter.

A useful pocket instrument, suitable for moisture determination of honey is made by Messrs Bellingham and Stanley Ltd., Hornsey Rise, London, N.19. This instrument is calibrated for use at 20° C. so that the temperature at the time of any observation must be carefully noted and the appropriate correction applied.

The method of use is given in a leaflet issued with the instrument.

Moisture content, refractive index and specific gravity when determined by means of a refractometer must be indicated as refractometric equivalents.

The refractometer method has the advantage of being speedy, accurate, and requiring, literally, only a drop of honey.

The specific gravity and water content of honey may also be determined by means of a hydrometer. The hydrometer consists of a floating glass tube, weighted at one end. When inserted into a container of honey the instrument comes to rest at a level corresponding to the specific gravity of the sample.

Hydrometers are calibrated for use at specific temperatures so that the temperature of the honey sample must be noted carefully and the appropriate correction made.

A suitable hydrometer for honey, covering the range of specific gravities from 1·350 to 1·450 is made by Messrs Burtt and Son, Stroud Road, Gloucester.

The determination of specific gravity by means of the hydrometer is a somewhat slow process and requires care and patience if any degree of accuracy is to be obtained. At best, results can be considered only as useful approximations.

When using the hydrometer the honey is most conveniently contained in a small gravity jar. This is a glass jar of about 2 inches diameter and about 6 inches high. It provides ample room for the hydrometer and the readings are easily seen.

Method

1. The instrument, jar and honey must have acquired a uniform temperature by standing in a reasonably warm room for some hours.
2. Make sure that both instrument and jar are dry then pour the honey carefully, down the side, into the gravity jar.
3. Take the temperature of the honey.
4. Insert the hydrometer, slowly, so that the reading shown is slightly above that expected, i.e. 1·415, and allow the instrument to settle (2 to 3 minutes). Make sure that the hydrometer does not touch the sides of the jar.
5. Note reading.
6. Gently raise the hydrometer a little and again allow it to settle.
7. Note reading.
8. The two readings should agree: if not, repeat the technique, allowing more time for the hydrometer to settle.
9. Correct the readings to 60° F., i.e. if the instrument is calibrated for that temperature, as is usual. For every degree above 60° F. add 0·00033: for every degree below 60° F. subtract 0·00033.

Technique No. 13

CHROMATOGRAPHIC ANALYSIS OF HONEY

Although the principle of chromatographic analysis is not new it is only within recent years that techniques of paper partition chromatography have been fully developed for analytical purposes.

Chromatographic analysis makes use of the fact that certain solvents flowing over a substance, such as a mixture of sugars as in honey, deposited on a suitable transporting medium (filter paper), carry the component substances different distances from the starting point where the mixture has been applied.

After a period of time, say from 24 to 40 hours, the paper is dried then sprayed with a suitable reagent in order to make visible the areas where the constituent substances are placed.

The ratio of the distance covered by the substance to the distance covered by the solvent is known as the Rf value. This Rf value is characteristic for different substances and makes possible the identification of components in a mixture. Rf values vary with different solvents.

It is also possible to define distances covered by various sugars, such as appear in honey, in relation to the distance covered by say glucose: such values are known as the Rg values. With regard to the normal sugars found in honey these values are:

Sugar	Rg Value
Maltose	0·32
Sucrose	0·5
Laevulose	1·38

as determined by the method of analysis outlined below.

The strips of filter paper containing the substance to be analysed are ‘developed’ in a large glass tank. The one I use is an old accumulator tank and measures $18 \times 9 \times 11$ inches, but specially made tanks of varying size can be readily purchased.

The solvent is contained in a small glass trough which sits on two glass rods suspended from the sides of the tank by rubber stoppers.

One end of the strip of filter paper dips into the trough, the paper being suspended over the edge and hanging down into the tank. The top of the tank is covered by a suitable piece of thick glass and the joint made gas tight, by means of vaseline.

Method

1. Cut a strip of filter paper, Whatman No. 1, of suitable length and width for the tank and trough in use. Serrate the lower edge to facilitate dripping.
2. About 2 to 3 inches from one end draw, with a pencil, a starting line.
3. Prepare the honey soln. about 1 gm. to 5 cc. water.
4. Take up a drop of the honey soln. in a micro-pipette made by drawing out a piece of glass tubing to form a capillary tube.
5. Deposit this drop on the starting line so that it spreads out to a diameter of about 5 cm.
6. Allow to dry and give an identification mark.
7. Run a control mixture, or mixtures, as another spot, or spots, alongside. Several samples may be run at the same time in which case the spots should be placed along the starting line at intervals of about $1\frac{1}{2}$ to 2 inches.
8. Fill the solvent trough with the appropriate solvent (see below) and carefully place the end of the strip of filter paper into the trough weighting it down with a piece of glass rod. The solvent will creep up the paper and syphon off into the tank.
9. Place the lid in position and make sure it is gas tight.
10. Allow the chromatogram to develop for about 72 hours.
11. Remove the paper from the tank and dry in a current of warm air. (A hair drier is useful here.)
12. Spray the paper with the spray reagent (see below). The paper should be suspended in front of a large sheet of glass, set up to the light so that the area sprayed is easily seen. Do not overspray. Any small scent spray type of atomiser is suitable.
13. Dry in an oven at 100° C. for 5 to 15 minutes (or carefully in front of an electric fire).

When the paper is dry the different sugars present appear as brown spots and take up different positions on the paper. If separate controls are run it will be found that the known sugars are ' partnered ', (or not) by the sugars contained in the mixture so that the sugars present are at once identified by their partners.

The following solvent and spray reagent are suitable for honey analysis.

Solvent.	Ethyl acetate	3 vol.
	Acetic acid	1 vol.
	Water	3 vol.

The mixture is shaken and allowed to settle into two layers: the upper layer is used.

Spray Reagent. 4 gm. P-anisidine hydrochloride
10 mls. water
10 mls. ethyl alcohol
80 mls. butyl alcohol
dissolve thoroughly

Owing to oxidation, the paper rapidly discolours and it is an advantage to ring round the spots with pencil if it is intended to keep the chromatogram for some time.

STATISTICAL TECHNIQUES

The science of statistics is one which is looked upon with more than suspicion by many people. It is asserted by some that there are three types of lie: the white lie, the black lie and, statistics. Or again, it is said that figures can be made to prove anything.

Another common statement is that figures cannot lie: however, it is more accurate to go further and say that liars can figure. The following proof that $2 = 1$ will illustrate this point and although we have some *a priori* evidence that this statement is absurd the flaw in the mathematical proof of a statement may not always be so obvious as in this particular instance.

Proof that $2 = 1$.

1. Let $a = b$.
2. Multiply both sides of the equation by a: giving $a^2 = ab$.
3. Subtract b^2 from both sides giving $a^2 - b^2 = ab - b^2$.
4. Factorise: giving $(a-b)(a+b) = b(a-b)$.
5. Divide by $(a-b)$ giving $a+b = b$; since, however, $a = b$ we have $2 = 1$.

The science of statistics, however, aims at testing statements and assessing or weighing evidence brought forward in support of any hypothesis.

It is relatively easy to formulate an hypothesis: easier still to produce evidence in support of it but such evidence must be tested if the correct interpretation is to be placed upon the data obtained.

In the science of beekeeping, statistical techniques can be applied when dealing with problems involving (*a*) distribution and measures of dispersion, e.g. in determining the water content or specific gravity of honey, perhaps of differing type, different season and different country, (*b*) correlation, e.g. association of rainfall and sunshine and flora of any specific locality to honey yield, etc., (*c*) sampling, e.g. the taking of a sample of bees from a colony when making a routine check for the presence of disease (d) significance, e.g. assessing the degree of reliability that can be placed on any experimental data obtained, i.e. estimating to what degree chance has played a part in the result obtained.

The average

One of the most commonly used mathematical terms is the ' average ' and the most common average is known as the arithmetic mean. Beekeepers frequently quote a figure for their average production but a simple statement of a particular value is, strictly speaking, of limited use in that it conveys only a limited amount of information. If any conclusion is to be drawn from a set of values it is necessary that the fullest intelligence be contained in the data presented.

Consider the following example as given by Levy and Preidl.[27]

Let us take two sets of figures, each set containing three groups from which we note that in each case the average value is 100.

Group ' A '
$$99 \cdot 9$$
$$100 \cdot 0$$
$$100 \cdot 1$$
$$\overline{300 \cdot 0 \div 3} \text{ average of 100}$$

Group ' B '
$$0 \cdot 1$$
$$100 \cdot 0$$
$$199 \cdot 9$$
$$\overline{300 \cdot 0 \div 3} \text{ average of 100.}$$

In other words the average alone does not tell us anything about the values comprising the group.

In group ' A ' all the values lie *close to the average*, whereas in group ' B ' they are *widely dispersed*.

When interpreting the values in any group it is necessary to know precisely how and to what degree the individual values differ from one another, i.e. we must know the degree of dispersion in the distribution.

This information can be conveyed by means of a parameter known as the Standard Deviation or root mean squared deviation. An example will make this clear.

K

Consider again the figures given in group 'A' set out as follows:

Number	Deviation from 100 i.e. the average	Deviation^2
99·9	−0·1	0·01
100·0	0·0	0·0
100·1	0·1	0·01
300·0		0·02

The standard deviation is determined by taking the square root of the sum of the squared deviates and dividing by the number of terms in the group.

$$\text{e.g. S.D.} = \sqrt{\frac{0·02}{3}}$$

$$= \pm 0·082$$

It should be noted that the average is such a value that the algebraic sum of the deviates = 0.

Further a deviation may be either side of the average so that the value ascertained for any S.D. since it is a square root is expressed as a $\pm$ term.

From this example it will be seen that the values in the group all cluster closely round the mean so that when we are told that the mean and standard deviation for a certain set of values is 100 and 0·082 we know at once that all values lie fairly close to the mean value.

Consider now the figures given in group 'B'.

Number	Deviation from 100 i.e. the average	Deviation^2
0·1	99·9	9980·01
100·0	0·0	0·0
199·9	99·9	9980·01
300·0		19,960·02

$$\text{As before the S.D.} = \sqrt{\frac{19,960·02}{3}}$$

$$= \pm 81·568.$$

It is immediately clear that on being given a mean of 100 and a Standard Deviation of 81·568, the values in the distribution are widely dispersed.

Thus, considering the two groups of values it is at once apparent that the mean values alone convey little information but, accompanied by the S.D. an accurate basis of comparison is at once offered.

A clearer idea of what is meant by a distribution may be obtained if, for example, we imagine a class of twenty entries in the light honey class at a show. Suppose we wish to obtain some idea of the uniformity of quality among the entries so far as specific gravity is concerned and from our measurements we find that:

2 exhibits show values lying between 1·381 and 1·390
2   ,,   ,,   ,,   ,,   ,,   1·391 ,, 1·400
8   ,,   ,,   ,,   ,,   ,,   1·401 ,, 1·410
6   ,,   ,,   ,,   ,,   ,,   1·411 ,, 1·420
2   ,,   ,,   ,,   ,,   ,,   1·421 ,, 1·430

These data may be set out in the form of a histogram (Fig. 36), where we have a clear picture of the manner in which the values are distributed. The distribution obtained from this small number of samples is, clearly, not quite ' uniform ' but if we had increased the number of our measurements, the distribution, assuming we were still sampling from the show bench, would nearly approach symmetry. It must be remembered, of course, that not all distributions are symmetrical in form since some may be what the statistician calls ' skewed ' positively or negatively but further discussion on that topic is outwith the scope of this note.

In our particular example we say that the class showing specific gravities of 1·401 to 1·410 is the Modal class since, as it were, it is the most fashionable.

When evaluated, our small group of show bench samples gives a mean value of 1·407 with a standard deviation of ±0·11.

It is found that in a symmetrical distribution (Fig. 37) 68% of all values lie within 1 σ of the mean (the Greek letter σ is the conventional sign taken to represent the standard deviation) while 94% lie within 2 σ of the mean.

For all practical purposes it could be taken that in our light honey class for this particular show and on this particular occasion 68% of the specific gravity values would lie between 1·396 and 1·418. It is assumed for the purpose of this example that these values are corrected to 60° F.

A practical comment resulting from such an exercise would be that the quality of this light honey class as a whole, was not good, since a reasonable standard specific gravity value at 60° F. for light honey is about 1·415±0·009.

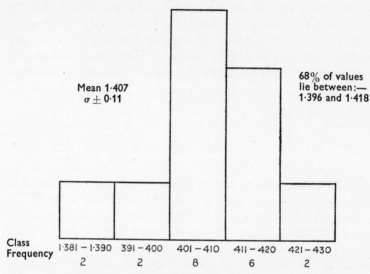

Mean 1·407
σ ± 0·11

68% of values
lie between:—
1·396 and 1·418

Class
Frequency

1·381 – 1·390	391 – 400	401 – 410	411 – 420	421 – 430
2	2	8	6	2

FIG. 36.   Histogram showing distribution of values for specific gravity
of 20 honey samples.

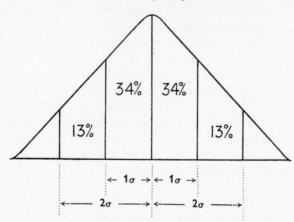

34% 34%

13% 13%

← 1σ → ← 1σ →

←——— 2σ ———→ ←——— 2σ ———→

FIG. 37.   In a symmetrical distribution, 68% of all values lie within
1σ of mean ; 94% lie within 2σ of mean.

When handling large numbers of terms and no mechanical aids are available the work involved can be most arduous and may lead to errors of various kinds. Statisticians have devised many ' tricks ' in order to lighten the burden of calculation. One such trick can be neatly employed in determining the mean and standard deviation of our honey samples.

A glance at the histogram shows that the mean will lie somewhere within the class 1·401 to 1·410. If we *assume* the mean to be 1·410 we can set out the figures as follows taking for each class a mid-point.

Class mid-point	Frequency	Difference from mean	Freq. × Dev.
385	2	−25	−50
395	2	−15	−30
405	8	− 5	−40
415	6	+ 5	+30
425	2	+15	+30
	20	algebraic sum	−60

If we divide the algebraic sum of the Freq. × Deviation column by the total number of samples in the distribution we get

$$\frac{-60}{20} = -3$$

i.e. the true mean is the assumed mean less (in this case) the obtained deviation, or 1·410 − 0·003 = 1·407.

The standard deviation can be calculated if the figures are set out as follows:

Class	Freq.	Dev.	Dev.^{2}	Freq. × Dev.^{2}
385	2	−22	484	968
395	2	−12	144	288
405	8	− 2	4	32
415	6	8	64	384
425	2	18	324	648
	20			2320

$$\text{i.e. } \sigma = \sqrt{\frac{2320}{20}}$$

$$\sigma = \sqrt{116}$$

i.e. 10·75 or for all practical purposes 11.

i.e. the Standard Deviation ± 0·11.

Correlation

Correlation concerns the relationship between two variables and is an important branch of statistical analysis. It is, however, vital, to appreciate that there must be a clear cause and effect relationship between the variables studied. As Sutton [20] has pointed out many examples of high correlation reflect nothing more than the fact that two series of numbers increase or decrease simultaneously, e.g. the correlation between the number of radio licences issued in Great Britain between 1935 and 1946 and the number of mental defectives notified during the same period is 0·91. Perfect correlation would have a value of unity.

Clearly such a correlation is meaningless but one might be on safer ground in correlating the number of murders and cases of violence with the number of T.V. licences issued within the last decade. It is of the greatest importance to be certain of the validity of a cause and effect relationship if a correct deduction is to be drawn from data presented in connection with any particular problem of correlation.

The degree of correlation between variables is expressed as the coefficient of correlation and is conveniently expressed as 'r'. For methods of calculating 'r' the reader is referred to any of the many text books available on statistical methods but a general idea of what this concept means can be had by considering the following sets of variables. These may well represent units of sunshine against units of honey produced during the honey season.

$$\text{Let } x = 3 \quad 5 \quad 7 \quad 9$$
$$y = 5 \quad 9 \quad 12 \quad 18$$

If these values are plotted as a graph it will be seen that the points lie more or less on a straight line and will give a value for 'r' of about 0·98 thus indicating a high degree of relationship.

On the other hand if the following values are plotted it will be found that they are widely scattered or dispersed and give a correlation coefficient of about 0·01.

$$\text{Let } x = 1 \quad 2·5 \quad 2·75 \quad 4$$
$$y = 2 \quad 2 \quad 4 \quad 2$$

The value of 'r' obtained gives us some indication of the degree of correlation but the reliability of our conclusion is

subject to the number of observations made. It may be taken
that the smaller the number of observations the higher must the
value of 'r' be in order to be statistically significant.

Statistical significance

If figures are not to lie or, more accurately, be misinterpreted,
it is necessary to apply some form of test in order to determine
whether or not the results obtained could have happened purely
by chance.

Frequently, in a scientific paper dealing with some or other
aspect of bee research one sees, after a set of values or statement,
$P = 0.05$ or $P < 0.001$. This is simply an indication of the
reliability or degree of confidence that can be placed in the results:
e.g. where $P = 0.05$ (1 in 20) the reliability indicated is that the
chances are 1 in 20 against the result obtained being due merely
to chance. Similarly $P = 0.01$ indicates a 1 in 100 chance,
$P = 0.001$ a 1 in 1000 chance while $P < 0.001$ means that the
result obtained would occur by chance with a probability of less
than 1 in 1000.

Thus, data may be tested at various levels, the lowest usually
being that of the 5% or 0.05, i.e. 1 in 20. Obviously the lower the
level the less reliable the result. The 5% level is usually taken to
be the lowest level at which some credence may be attached to the
results obtained in any experiment.

However, if on testing, data do not approach the 5% level
of significance it does not mean that the result obtained is false:
all that is indicated is that the result is *unlikely* to be accurate and
further work must necessarily be done on the project before any
definite conclusion may be drawn.

In illustration a simple and useful test may be made of figures
obtained from trials of two different methods of honey production,
assuming of course that factors such as colony strength, bee flora,
etc. were as nearly as possible equal for both groups.

The systems are designated 'A' and 'B'.

System 'A'

No. of Colonies 40
Average production
50 lbs. ± 10 lbs.

System 'B'

No. of Colonies 60
Average production
45 lbs. ± 6 lbs.

Can we say from these values that system 'A' is superior to system 'B' or vice versa?

To test this we calculate what is known as the Standard Error of the Mean.

$$\text{The formula is: s.e. mean} = \sqrt{\frac{\sigma_1^2}{n_1} + \frac{\sigma_2^2}{n_2}}$$

$$= \sqrt{\frac{10^2}{40} + \frac{6^2}{60}}$$

$$= \sqrt{3\cdot 1}$$

$$= 1\cdot 732$$

The difference between the means is 5 and this must now be divided by the s.e. mean giving:

$$\frac{5}{1\cdot 732} = 2\cdot 882$$

If the $\dfrac{\text{diff. of means}}{\text{s.e. mean}}$ is less than 2 the difference between the sample means is *not* statistically significant. In other words a result of two times the s.e. mean is equal to an odds against the result being due to chance of 21 to 1. The value of $2\cdot 882$ is equivalent to an odds against of approx. 300 to 1.

Another test of statistical significance which has wide application is the χ^2 test (pronounced kye as in broad Scots for cows, is a letter from the Greek alphabet and is the conventional sign for this form of test).

The χ^2 test compares the observed frequencies of functions with the frequency calculated for a given distribution. This may be made clearer by taking the well known example of tossing a coin. The concept in this case will be easier to grasp since we have some *a priori* evidence that, assuming the coin is not biased, heads and tails will occur an equal number of times if a reasonably large number of tosses is made.

Suppose a coin is tossed 50 times: we would expect approximately 25 heads and 25 tails to result. Instead, however, we find heads occur only 15 times. Is this result due to chance or is the coin biased?

In applying the test the data are set out as follows:

Expected frequency of heads is 25.
Expected frequency of tails is 25
Observed frequency of heads is 15.
Observed frequency of tails is 35

The formula is $\chi^2 = \sum \dfrac{(O-E)^2}{E}$

i.e. the sum of the difference between the observed and expected frequencies divided by the expected frequency.

In our case:

$$\chi^2 = \frac{(35-25)^2}{25} + \frac{(15-25)^2}{25}$$

$$= \frac{100}{25} + \frac{100}{25}$$

$$= 8$$

Reference must now be made to a table of χ^2 in order to determine whether or not the value could have arisen by chance (see Statistical Tables).

In the jargon of the statistician these tables must be entered with one or more ' degrees of freedom '. This ' freedom ' refers to the number of classes whose frequency may be given arbitrary values. When considering the concept of an average it was noted that the algebraic sum of the deviates from the average must be 0, thus, in evaluating χ^2 the calculation is made on one value less than the total number of independent values, in other words N—1 values. The consideration of a distribution entails the calculation of one or more functions and the number of degrees of freedom is taken to be the number of values less the number of functions being determined.

In our example the χ^2 table is entered with one degree of freedom and we find that the value to be reached for P to equal 0·05, is 3·84: for P to equal 0·01, 6·64 and for P to equal 0·001, 10·83.

Thus there is some cause for thinking that this coin might just be biased since it does not make the 0·001 level of significance but to be more certain in the matter the experiment would have to be extended. Further analysis would then give stronger evidence one way or the other.

Another application of the χ^2 test can be made, e.g. when one wishes to test results obtained in a disease control experiment. Suppose in such an experiment, in an untreated apiary 11 out of 12 colonies were infested, say with acarine disease, while one remained healthy.

Under the same conditions in a treated apiary of 11 colonies 7 responded and became healthy while 4 remained in the diseased state.

These data may be set out in what is known as a 2×2 contingency table, as follows:

	healthy	infested	total
control	1 (a)	11 (b)	12 (a+b)
treated	7 (c)	4 (d)	11 (c+d)
total	8 (a+c)	15 (b+d)	23 (N)

In this case our χ^2 formula is:

$$= \frac{(ad-bc-\frac{1}{2}N)^2\,N}{(a+c)(b+d)(c+a)(a+b)}$$

thus from our figures we have:

$$\frac{(4-77-11\cdot5)^2\times23}{8\times15\times11\times12}$$

$$= 10\cdot35$$

Entering our tables with one degree of freedom we find that for P to equal 0·001 a value of 10·83 must be obtained. While our result does not quite reach this figure we would be on fairly good grounds for concluding that the bees had been cured as a result of our treatment and that the possibility of the cure being due to chance was remote: in fact the odds against being almost 1000 to 1.

To take another example of this neat application of the test.

Suppose in a swarm control experiment two systems are tested, ' A ' and ' B '.

In system ' A ' out of 200 colonies 24 swarmed.

In system ' B ' out of 200 colonies 9 swarmed. Is system ' B ' superior to ' A ' or is the result obtained fortuitous?

Setting out our table as before we have:

	system ' A '	system ' B '	total
swarmed	24	9	33
not swarmed	176	191	361
total	200	200	400

On the above figures the χ^2 value works out at 6·5 so that we should be justified in suggesting that system ' B ' *was* superior, under the conditions applicable during the test but further experiment would, of course, be desirable in order to strengthen our conclusion.

The χ^2 test may, again, be applied to the following set of circumstances.

Supposing five different out apiary sites are being tried and that the particular season in question has been very poor since average yields are of the order of 14, 17, 13, 16 and 25 lbs. On the basis of this result, in what could be considered an almost disastrous season, can we take it that one site is better than another? If we postulate the null hypothesis, i.e. that there is *no* difference between the locations we imply that there *should* have been an average yield of exactly

$$\frac{14-17-13-16-25}{5} = 17 \text{ lbs.}$$

Taking the formula for $\chi^2 = \sum \dfrac{(O-E)^2}{E}$
we have the following:

Observed	Expected	Difference	Difference²
14	17	−3	9
17	17	0	0
13	17	−4	16
16	17	−1	1
25	17	8	64

thus: $\chi^2 = \sum \dfrac{9}{17} + \dfrac{0}{17} + \dfrac{16}{17} + \dfrac{1}{17} + \dfrac{64}{17} = 5\cdot3$

If now, we enter the χ^2 tables at 4 degrees of freedom we find that to reach even the 5% level of significance a value of 9·49 must be obtained. On the value obtained the 5% level is not reached so that the null hypothesis is accepted.

Further trials would, of course, be helpful but we would be fairly safe to conclude, on the existing evidence, that there was little to choose between the various apiary sites.

The Poisson Distribution

Another statistical distribution known as the Poisson Distribution can be of use in testing the accuracy of a technique, such as is used for the determination of the absolute number of pollen grains in a sample of honey.

The Poisson Distribution makes use of a mathematical constant ' e ' which is the base of natural or Napierian logarithms and allows us to calculate the probability of the occurrence of any event. The series is:

$$e^{-z} \left(1 + z + \frac{z^2}{2!} + \frac{z^3}{3!} + \frac{z^4}{4!} + \ldots\ldots\frac{z^n}{n!} \right)$$

Applying this to the pollen counting technique we find that over 40 cells counted, the average number of grains per cell is 3. i.e. $z = 3$ and (from tables) $e^{-3} = 0\cdot0498$ or for all practical purposes $0\cdot05$

Our series now reads:

$$0\cdot05 \left(1 + 3 + \frac{3^2}{2!} + \frac{3^3}{3!} + \frac{3^4}{4!} + \frac{3^5}{5!} + \frac{3^6}{6!} \right)$$